The Orchid Paintings of
# Franz Bauer

Franz Bauer in middle age. Oil painting by an unknown artist
(Royal Botanic Gardens, Kew)

# The Orchid Paintings of
# Franz Bauer

Joyce Stewart and William T. Stearn

THE HERBERT PRESS *in association with*
The Natural History Museum, London

First published in Great Britain 1993 by
The Herbert Press Ltd, 46 Northchurch Road, London N1 4EJ
in association with The Natural History Museum, London

House Editors: Julia MacKenzie and Brenda Herbert
Designed by Pauline Harrison

Set in Bembo
by Nene Phototypesetters Ltd, Northampton

Printed and bound in Hong Kong
by South China Printing Company (1988) Ltd

A CIP catalogue record for this book is available from the
British Library.

ISBN 1–871569–58–3

ACKNOWLEDGEMENTS

The authors and publisher would like to thank Malcolm
Beasley and Julia Hickey of the Botany Library, The Natural
History Museum, London and Dr Helmut Rohlfing of the
University Library, Göttingen, for their very helpful
co-operation in the selection of the illustrations for this book.

The frontispiece and the illustrations on pages 6 and 17 are
copyright of the Trustees of The Royal Botanic Gardens,
Kew © 1993.

The illustrations on pages 75, 77, 79, 81, 93, 97, 103, 109,
and 129 are © the Niedersächsische Staats- und
Universitätsbibliothek, Göttingen.

The remainder of the illustrations are © The Natural History
Museum, London.

# Contents

Francis Bauer (1758–1840),
Kew's first botanical artist
*by* William T. Stearn  *page* 7

The structure and
function of orchid flowers
*by* Joyce Stewart  *page* 19

A selection of
Franz Bauer's orchid paintings
*by* Joyce Stewart and William T. Stearn  *page* 39

Bibliography and
further reading lists  *page* 154

Index  *page* 157

25 · 4 · 34

Franz Bauer at the age of 75. Drawing by W. Brockenden, 23 August 1834
(Royal Botanic Gardens, Kew)

# Francis Bauer (1758–1840)
# Kew's First Botanical Artist

*by* William T. Stearn

Lthough Francis Bauer (1758–1840) has never obtained the popularity as a painter of flowers granted to his contemporary Pierre-Joseph Redouté (1759–1840), because so little of his work has been published, he nevertheless stands eminent in a period of botanical art made celebrated also by Ferdinand Bauer, his brother, James Sowerby, Sydenham Edwards, Pierre Turpin and Redouté. The present volume contains almost all of his portraits of *Orchidaceae*, a family which attracted him as much by the intricacy and diversity of its flowers as by their beauty. They represent only a part, albeit typical and significant, of his artistic output during some fifty-years residence in Kew; this has laid hidden in London and Göttingen for 150 years and accordingly has been little appreciated.

Nevertheless, Francis Bauer's work has always been esteemed by those with access to it. The great German botanical bibliographer Georg August Pritzel (1815–74) examined some 1,500 botanical works in the course of compiling his monumental *Thesaurus Literaturae botanicae* (1847–52; second edition 1871–82) and his likewise monumental *Iconum botanicarum Index locupletissimus* (1854–55). He gave special attention to illustrated books, as his *Index* of illustrations makes evident. No one of his time knew such books so well and no one then could better assess their quality. This extensive experience lies behind the entry in his *Thesaurus*: '**Bauer**, *Franz*, der grösste Pflanzenmaler'. Although thus to designate Franz (later Francis) Andreas Bauer as 'the greatest plant artist' seems unjust towards his equally skilled and much more adventurous brother Ferdinand Lucas Bauer (1760–1826), in 1950 Wilfrid Blunt endorsed Pritzel's verdict. He also remarked that 'the last hundred years show no artist of the calibre of either of these two brilliant brothers'. Since 1950 only a few artists have produced work approaching theirs. Pritzel's successor as a botanical bibliographer, Claus Nissen (1901–76), in his *Die botanische Buchillustration* (1951) wrote that 'es schien lediglich zweifelhaft ob er oder sein Bruder der bedeutendere sei' [it seems altogether quite doubtful whether he or his brother is the more important]. Undoubtedly the work of the two Bauer brothers will not be easily equalled, and never be surpassed, in elegance and exactitude. Both illustrated orchids, Franz mostly wild British orchids and the species cultivated at Kew, Ferdinand those he saw growing wild in the eastern Mediterranean region and in Australia.

## PARENTAGE AND UPBRINGING

LUCAS BAUER (died 1761), court painter and gallery curator to the Prince of Liechtenstein, and his wife Theresia had three sons, Josef Anton (born 1756), Franz Andreas (born 1758) and Ferdinand Lucas (born 1760), all talented. Their birthplace was Feldsberg, Lower Austria, which, on the break-up of the Austro-Hungarian Empire after World War I, was incorporated in the newly formed republic of Czechoslovakia and received the Czech name Valtice. Here was a Liechtenstein family mansion with an extensive park in which they must have first become acquainted with wild flowers.

Far away in Luxembourg and almost contemporaneous with the birth of the three Bauer boys, a painter named Charles-Joseph Redouté (died 1776) and his wife Marguerite produced three sons: Antoine-Ferdinand (born 1756), Pierre-Joseph (born 1759) and Henri-Joseph (born 1766); they likewise inherited their father's artistic talent but nothing else. Pierre and Henri Redouté, Franz and Ferdinand Bauer, these four became the most distinguished natural-history artists of their period, the late eighteenth century and the early nineteenth century.

Obviously Charles-Joseph Redouté instructed artistically his three sons, but Lucas Bauer died too soon to teach his. The three fatherless Bauer boys came under the care and instruction of a very remarkable man, Norbert Boccius (1729–1806), a prior of the monastery and hospital of the Barmherzige Brüder (the Merciful Brothers) at Feldsberg. A theologian, a qualified physician and a lover of plants and art, he educated the Bauer boys and employed them to illustrate plants for his collection. The results of their labours exist in the Liechtensteinische Bibliothek in Vienna as fourteen volumes containing 2,250 illustrations. The botanical world should honour the memory of this kind long-forgotten Feldsberg monk.

## EARLY YEARS IN VIENNA

THE PRINCE OF LIECHTENSTEIN sent Josef Anton to Rome to study art and later made him curator of his gallery; seemingly thereafter he contributed nothing to botanical illustration. Franz and Ferdinand sought employment as artists in Vienna. Here Franz became flower-painter to a Count Dietrichstein. Presumably he and Ferdinand were introduced by Boccius to the professor Nicolaus von Jacquin (1727–1817), who employed them both, together with other artists, to illustrate the sumptuous folio works he was producing on new and little-known plants. The son of a wealthy cloth manufacturer of French origin, Jacquin was born and educated in Leiden, then enticed in 1752 by Gerard van Swieten, also a Dutchman, to continue his medical studies in Vienna. Van Swieten, as personal physician to the Empress Maria Theresia, obviously possessed much influence at the imperial court. Jacquin, his protegé, rose to be Professor of Botany and Director of the botanic garden in Vienna, into which an inflow of new and rare plants, notably from South Africa, provided abundant material for description and illustration. He recognized the talent of the two brothers and employed first Ferdinand, and later Franz, to prepare illustrations for his *Icones Plantarum rariorum* (3 vols, 1781–95). From Jacquin or Boccius or both they learned that botanical draughtsmanship demands understanding of the plant figured, even down to minute detail, as well as its portrayal with accuracy and grace; thereby they were initiated into the intricacies of plant form. Under such supervision they became accustomed to precise observation and developed superb techniques of drawing and colouring. Jacquin was himself an able botanical artist but his teaching and administrative duties gave him no time for illustrating plants except in correspondence with Sir Joseph Banks's librarian Jonas Dryander. Having trained them so well, Jacquin then lost the services of both. Two members of the wealthy cultured English landed gentry lured them from Vienna. John Sibthorp took Ferdinand away on his travels. Sir Joseph Banks later induced Franz to settle at Kew as his resident artist.

## FERDINAND BAUER AND JOHN SIBTHORP

CURIOUSLY ENOUGH an ancient manuscript herbal in Vienna indirectly influenced their careers, especially Ferdinand's. The big work on medicaments compiled in the first century AD by the Greek medical man Dioscorides dominated European pharmacy down to the seventeenth century. The identification of the medicinal plants mentioned by him, which had a practical motive, greatly stimulated botany after 1516. 'For a whole century thereafter,' wrote E. L. Greene in 1909, 'the most voluminous and most useful books of botany were in the form of commentaries on Dioscorides. Such in large part are the works of Anguillara, Mattioli, Maranta, Dodoens, Cesalpino, Fabius Columna, and the Bauhins.' William Turner (*c*.1508–68) referred to the Bologna professor, Luca Ghini, as 'Lucas Gynus my master in Bonony [Bologna, ancient Bononia], the reader [i.e. lecturer] there in Dioscorides', which indicates the importance attached then to his text. Dioscorides had lived in the eastern Mediterranean region. John Sibthorp (1758–96), Professor of Botany at Oxford, apprehended clearly, as no one else seems to have done, that to recover for modern use the herb lore of the Ancient Greeks one must study at first hand the plants of Greece, the Aegean Archipelago and Asia Minor, all then under Turkish rule. Accordingly, he set out in 1784 on a Near Eastern research journey. From a medical standpoint this was already an anachronistic venture but it resulted in the magnificent *Flora Graeca* (10 vols, 1806–40) of Sibthorp and Smith, with illustrations by Ferdinand Bauer. First, however, Sibthorp visited Vienna. Here in the Imperial Library (now Österreichische Nationalbibliothek) was the earliest known illustrated codex of Dioscorides, the *Codex Aniciae Iulianae* or *Codex Vindobonensis*, with coloured illustrations invaluable, then as now, for interpreting the application of Dioscoridean names. Its study was Sibthorp's primary task preliminary to visiting Greece and Asia Minor.

Sibthorp met Jacquin and Boccius in Vienna and so became acquainted with Ferdinand Bauer. Obviously impressed by Bauer's talent he engaged him as artist for his Levantine expedition. Their journey took them through Italy and then to Crete and other Aegean Islands, Athens, the Bithynian Olympus, Constantinople (Istanbul), Smyrna (Izmir), Cyprus, etc. Fortunately Sibthorp's brother-in-law, John Hawkins (1761–1841), accompanied them. A Cornishman and landowner who had studied mining in Freiburg a.d. Oder, he spoke fluent German and treated Bauer as a friend. Their journey completed, Sibthorp and Hawkins returned to England, taking Bauer with them. He had made graphic material to be worked up into 1,000 coloured illustrations of plants, 363 of animals and 132 of landscapes. It should be noted that the localities on his original drawings at Oxford for the *Flora Graeca* are in Bauer's handwriting, not Sibthorp's, as is evident from the spelling: thus he used a *p* when an Englishman would have used a *b* and conversely a *b* instead of a *p*. His brother Franz always called their birthplace 'Feldsperg' not 'Feldsberg'. In Oxford he worked for years on completing his drawings for publication. Sibthorp, having contracted tuberculosis, died at Bath in 1796, but Hawkins as his executor took charge of Bauer's work and saw to the publication of the *Flora Graeca*.

## FRANZ BAUER, JACQUIN THE YOUNGER
## AND SIR JOSEPH BANKS

MEANWHILE FRANZ BAUER had worked as artist for Jacquin in Vienna. Jacquin's son Joseph Franz (1766–1839) inherited his botanical and chemical interests and became his successor. In 1788 he set out on a botanical Grand Tour, taking Franz with him. They travelled to England by way of Prague, Dresden, Halle, Berlin, Göttingen, Mainz, Leiden, Utrecht and Brussels, intending after a long stay in London to return to Vienna by way of Paris. Sir Joseph Banks (1743–1820) made them very welcome in London and gave them every facility for study in his extremely rich herbarium and library. These greatly impressed the younger Jacquin who wrote to his father from London on 16 December 1788 that the quantity of aids to botanical study and the indescribable zeal with which it was pursued made London in this respect the first place in the world. He added 'Wenn sie sonst noch Zweifel über Pflanzen haben, denn hier ist der Ort, wo man über alles Sicherheit erlangen kann.' [If you have moreover uncertainty regarding plants, then here is the place where one can above all reach certainty]. As has been said elsewhere (Stearn 1990), 'Banks was the first great English promoter of botanical illustration. No one before him employed so many artists in the portrayal of plants. He initiated botanical illustration at Kew.' Returned from his voyage to Newfoundland in 1766–67, he engaged the celebrated G. D. Ehret (1708–70) to illustrate his specimens (*see* Lysaght, 1971, for reproductions). He took Sydney Parkinson (*c.*1745–71) as natural history artist on Cook's voyage of world circumnavigation in the *Endeavour* 1768–71, and he employed five artists in London to complete Parkinson's drawings. Thanks to his enterprise the Royal Garden at Kew continually received new plants, and he needed a resident artist to record them. The artist accompanying the younger Jacquin, Franz Bauer, he shrewdly concluded, was the very man.

Jacquin saw that clearly. In a letter from London on 3 November 1789 to his brother Gottfried in Vienna he wrote: 'Complimente von Bauer. Ich glaube es ist höchste Zeit, dass ich ihn von hier wegbringe, sonst wird er mir abgefischt. Banks hat ausserordentlich Augen auf ihn.' [Compliments from Bauer. I believe it is high time I take him away from here, otherwise he will be filched from me. Banks has eyes very much upon him.] A sure position with a high salary, esteem, association with learned men, notably Banks himself and his Swedish botanist-librarian, Jonas Dryander, opportunity to practise his art without hindrance, a richly stocked botanic garden in which to work, contact with his brother Ferdinand in Oxford; all these Bauer had for the taking. Jacquin decided to go on to Paris. For Banks to engage Bauer's services it was now or never. Many years later Sir James Everard Home recounted the circumstances of his friend Bauer's intended departure for Paris: 'His passage was engaged and place taken by the coach in which he was to go the next morning to Dover; on the last day of his stay in London (I think Sunday), he had dined with Sir Joseph Banks, who after tea took him aside (into the Voyage Room) and made his proposals to remain in England, which he at last accepted.' (J. E. Home to Robert Brown, 17 December 1840; quoted by Meynell, 1983). Bauer had already portrayed *Calycanthus praecox* (now *Chimonanthus praecox*) for Banks. In December 1789 Jacquin was in London with Bauer. In February 1790 he was in Paris without him.

## RESIDENCE AT KEW

PROVIDED WITH a salary of £300 a year, Franz, his name soon anglicized to Francis, lived tranquilly at Kew for the next fifty years, patiently investigating and depicting its plants. Remote though he was in rural Kew from the tragic events of the Napoleonic Wars on the Continent, he must have contemplated with dismay the successive defeats of the Austrian army at Arcole, Hohenlinden, Ulm, Austerlitz and Wagram and the slaughter of so many of his compatriots.

Bauer's original unpublished illustrations of Kew plants at the Natural History Museum in South Kensington give the impression that he simply followed his own bent without any direction and purpose except that of satisfying his curiosity and creative urge. He became more and more fascinated by the complicated floral mechanisms of the *Asclepiadaceae* and *Orchidaceae*, by pollen grains and spores and by the histology and anatomy not only of plants but of animals. Whereas his brother Ferdinand had helped to explore distant lands, discovering and depicting species new to science, Franz patiently explored with microscope and scalpel the hidden parts of plants around him at Kew and found in them no less a wealth of material challenging his skill to record graphically and with understanding what few or none had seen before. Banks's library and herbarium were at Soho Square, London. When Robert Brown, who had travelled with Ferdinand Bauer on Flinders's voyage around Australia, became Curator and Librarian of Banksian collections, he directed Franz's attention to ferns. The drawings he made then for Brown and the other drawings made much later for Sir William Jackson Hooker were lithographed by W. H. Fitch for Hooker's *Genera Filicum* (1838–42).

At Kew Bauer could devote without interruption as many days as he pleased to depicting accurately, for example, the hundreds of small leaves on a South African species of *Erica*. Many such species had come into cultivation in England through the activity of Banks's Scottish plant collector Francis Masson (1741–1805) at the Cape of Good Hope between 1772 and 1774, 1786 and 1795. Bauer illustrated thirty species in his *Delineations of exotick Plants cultivated in the Royal Gardens at Kew, by Francis Bauer, Botanick Painter to His Majesty* (1796–1803). Banks evidently obtained this royal recognition for Bauer; he considered that these superb illustrations required no descriptive text, so there was none. 'Each figure is intended to answer itself every question a Botanist can wish to ask, respecting the structure of the plant.' A contemporary botanical artist, Henry Charles Andrews, published between 1802 and 1830 *Coloured Engravings of Heaths*, with 283 folio plates and descriptive text, and between 1804 and 1812 *The Heathery, or a Monograph of the Genus Erica*, with 300 octavo plates, which testify to the many species of the genus then skilfully grown in England. All three are fine works of great botanical value but Andrews's plates do not attain the perfection of Bauer's. However, Andrews, unlike privileged Francis Bauer, had to earn a living by selling his illustrated publications.

The extraordinary South African genus *Strelitzia*, which includes the bird-of-paradise flower, *S. reginae*, attracted Bauer's attention. Banks named this genus and species in honour of Queen Charlotte (1744–1818), who before her marriage to George III had been Princess Charlotte-Sophia of Mecklenburg-Strelitz, a small north German duchy. Queen Charlotte, apparently a plain-featured woman whose major achievement was to bear fifteen children, is more appropriately commemorated by a London maternity hospital named Queen Charlotte's Hospital than she is by such a conspicuous flower. Obviously at Banks's instigation, Bauer published in 1818 *Strelitzia depicta* with four coloured plates.

Queen Charlotte and Princess Elizabeth (1770–1840), her second daughter, received lessons in painting from Bauer; his only reward was a stick of Indian ink! A much more important pupil was William Hooker (1779–1832), who should *not* be confused with William Jackson Hooker (1785–1865), from 1841 to 1865 Director of the Royal Botanic Gardens, Kew, who was also a skilled botanical artist. William Hooker provided the botanical illustrations and Richard Anthony Salisbury the text to the *Paradisus Londinensis* (1805–11); he also illustrated F. Pursh's *Flora Americae Septentrionalis*. On the title page of the *Paradisus Londinensis* he described himself as having been 'Pupil of Francis Bauer Esq., Botanic Painter to their Majesties', an inscription which testifies both to the celebrity Bauer had attained and Hooker's pride in having been taught by such a master. Bauer's influence is evident not only in Hooker's careful botanical illustrations, but above all in his beautiful and meticulous paintings of fruits, which place him as high among pomological artists as the Bauers among botanical artists (cf. Stearn, 1989). Unfortunately ill health struck him down at the height of his artistic achievement.

## BAUER'S STUDY OF ORCHIDS

DURING BAUER'S long association with Kew the methods of glasshouse heating changed dramatically, as did the kinds of glasshouse plants. Hot dry air and flue systems, under which Cape heaths flourished and orchids died, gave place to heating by hot water circulating through cast-iron pipes and to better control of humidity. In the course of time the heated glasshouse became a happy home and not a slaughterhouse for tropical orchids. This horticultural success unfortunately led to ruthless collecting; one professional orchid collector in Colombia had 4,000 trees felled and a whole area devastated to get 10,000 plants of *Odontoglossum crispum* for sale in Europe. In 1789 the first edition of Aiton's *Hortus Kewensis* recorded thirty-six species of *Orchidaceae* as cultivated at Kew or within the London area; of these all but three were terrestrial orchids from Europe (23 British, 2 non-British), North America (5) and Cape of Good Hope (3); only three (West Indies 2, China 1) were tropical. Bauer seems to have begun his portrayal of them, together with investigation of their floral structure, about 1791 and continued this at least until 1829 according to his dated drawings. The most conspicuous orchid available in 1789 was *Phaius tancarvilleae* (then called *Bletia tankervilleae*) introduced from China by John Fothergill about 1778.

By 1813, when Robert Brown published an account of cultivated *Orchidaceae* in the second edition of the *Hortus Kewensis* (5: 188–222), he listed 113 species, of which twenty-six were tropical species from the West Indies; there were now sixteen species from North America, twelve from New South Wales and five from India. This remarkable increase provided Bauer with yet more alluring orchid material for study and illustration. Many of his drawings are dated. These dates reveal that by 1801 he had already painted *Cymbidium ensifolium* and by 1811 several British orchids. Ultimately he portrayed species from Ecuador, India, Jamaica, Mexico and North America as well as Britain. All are depicted in accurate meticulous detail and at the same time are aesthetically pleasing. He was an expert dedicated microscopist intent on getting to know their inner as well as their outer formation; he made drawings of both.

Bauer's microscopical work was not exclusively on orchids or botanical. He advised the anatomist and physician Sir Everard Home (1765–1832) on microscopy and made drawings of microscopical details for his *Lectures on comparative Anatomy* (1814–28) and his papers in the *Philosophical Transactions of the Royal Society*, including the foot of the domestic fly as an animal able to walk defying gravity. He also illustrated Banks's 1807 paper on that pest of apple trees, the woolly aphis *(Eriosoma lanigerum).*

Meanwhile John Lindley (1799–1865), from being an assistant to Robert Brown in Banks's library and herbarium at Soho Square, London, a post he lost on Banks's death in 1820, had risen by 1830 to be Professor of Botany in the newly founded London University and editor of *The Botanical Register*, wherein his artist Miss Drake illustrated many orchids (cf. Stearn, 1990). He was also well on his way to becoming the world's leading orchidologist. Bauer lived at Eglantine Cottage on Kew Green. Lindley's house was at Turnham Green near the Horticultural Society's garden and he had only a short ride on horseback to Kew bridge and across the Thames to reach Bauer who certainly appreciated the friendship of learned men. Indeed, according to Scheer (1840), at Kew for some length of time, there 'used to meet here, almost every Saturday, at Mr Bauer's, many of the most eminent of men of the day, for purposes connected with Botany and other branches of Natural Philosophy, and a friendly and social intercourse.' By now Bauer had accumulated many drawings relating to the minute structure of orchids in the course of his studies with the microscope. Lindley, characteristically zealous and industrious, took in hand their publication. For these he provided text in association with Bauer. Lithography was then replacing copper engraving as a cheaper method of graphic reproduction. A skilled botanic draughtsman, Lindley himself lithographed some of Bauer's drawings; the celebrated professional lithographer M. Gauci did the others. Thus, thanks to Lindley's enterprise, Bauer saw his work reach the botanical public between 1830 and 1838 as *Illustrations of Orchidaceous Plants by Francis Bauer Esq. F.R.S., L.S. & H.S. with Notes and prefactory Remarks by John Lindley.* This has thirty-five lithographed folio plates, twenty-eight by Bauer, seven by Lindley, un-coloured or hand-coloured, illustrating floral structure, seeds and pollen. Bauer's relations with Robert Brown were not always easy; thus he wrote to Lindley on 7 February 1832, 'I wish you could contrive that Brown should not see the drawings before they are published.'

## LATER YEARS AT KEW

SIR JOSEPH BANKS died on 9 May 1820, his life having been replete with varied beneficent activities, some with long-lasting effect. An annuity of £300 a year now replaced Bauer's salary of £300 a year. His life seems to have continued tranquilly as before with painting Kew plants as his main occupation and using his Ploessel's Austrian-made microscope to aid his studies. A circle of friends, among them Lindley, Robert Brown, William Clift, William Townsend Aiton, John Smith the Kew gardener especially interested in ferns, Frederick Scheer, A. B. Granville and Sir James Everard Home, all men of distinction, saved him from being a lonely batchelor. Around Kew Green there were several German speakers, notably Scheer and Ernest Augustus Frederick Guelph (1771–1851), the Duke of Cumberland, who was the fifth son of George III and Queen Charlotte. All appear to have esteemed Bauer as an agreeable genial person of high intelligence as well as a superb artist and perceptive microscopist. He must have been well acquainted with the Duke of Cumberland. They had in common the German language and a love of Kew, where the Duke had been born and spent most of his life, enjoying its village nature, until he became King of Hanover in 1837; Salic law prevented his niece Victoria, who had become Queen of England, from inheriting the throne of Hanover. The Duke was an autocratic, tactless, bigoted, ferociously conservative and reactionary but nevertheless highly intelligent man, formerly a bold Hanoverian cavalry officer, who was so feared and detested by people in England that they were glad in 1837 to have him inflicted upon the people of Hanover. Presumably he treated Bauer with more respect than the seven distinguished Göttingen professors he sacked for voicing their liberal views, and in 1837 Bauer gave him a collection of drawings. This accounts for the large number of Franz Bauer's drawings in Göttingen. After Bauer's death, his eight portfolios marked 'Kew Plants' passed to the British Museum in Bloomsbury, London in accordance with his will of 8 October 1839 (cf. Meynell, 1983). They were later moved to the Museum's Natural History Departments at South Kensington. These drawings amounted to 1532, according to Robert Brown, and included many orchid paintings, some of which are reproduced in the present book. Bauer's remaining possessions were auctioned in November 1841 and the King of Hanover bought part of them. He presented this Bauer material from Kew, 'zu Erinnerung meines dortigen Aufenthalts' [in memory of my stay here], to the Göttingen University Library (Universitäts-Bibliothek) where they are in the manuscript collection (*Handschriften* 312–315, Hist. nat 94).

While Bauer was still living, his friend Frederick Scheer (*c.*1792–1868),

A memorial to Franz Bauer by Richard Westmacott Junior in St Anne's Church, Kew Green

a German merchant from Rügen who resided on Kew Green, stated in 1840 that 'Vanity, selfishness and illiberality were foreign to his disposition, as friends and strangers in great numbers can testify' and that the life of 'the Nestor of Kew' had been one 'of incessant activity, usefulness and greatness'. The Linnean Society of London recognized his scientific merit by electing him a Fellow in 1804, the tardy and unappreciative Royal Society of London not until 1821. He never married, but shortly before his death he adopted as his daughter Elizabeth Baker who had looked after him for some twenty-five years.

## MEMORIAL TO BAUER AT KEW

THE ESTEEM IN which his friends held Bauer inspired them to subscribe for an elaborate memorial to him in St Anne's Church on Kew Green. This was sculptured in marble by Richard Westmacott Junior, with a profile of Bauer at the top, the sides of the inscription ornate with magnoliaceous and *Banksia* foliage, and at the foot a palette, painter's brushes and wads of drawing paper. The inscription reads:

> In memory of Francis Bauer Esqr F.R.S. F.L.S. Botanical Painter to His Majesty George the Third and Resident Draughtsman for fifty years to the Royal Botanic Garden at Kew, where he devoted himself to the advancement of Natural Science under the munificent patronage of Sir Joseph Banks Bart. the President of the Royal Society.
>
> In the delineation of plants he united the accuracy of the profound naturalist with the skill of the accomplished artist to a degree which has been only equalled by his brother Ferdinand.
>
> In microscopical drawing he was altogether unrivalled and science will be ever indebted for his elaborate illustrations of animal and vegetable structures of which invaluable specimens are preserved in the British Museum and in the University of Göttingen.
>
> He was born 4th October 1758 at Feldsperg in Austria and accompanied his friend the Baron Joseph Jacquin to England in 1788.
>
> He settled in Kew in 1790, where he lived admired, loved and respected. He died 11th December 1840, aged 82 years. The works of Francis Bauer are his best monument. Friendship inscribes this record on his honored tomb.
> > "Lord, how manifold are Thy works, in wisdom hast
> > Thou made them all." Psalms CIV v.24

A century and a half since its inception, that remains a true and just tribute.

Bibliography: see page 154

# The structure and function of orchid flowers

*by* Joyce Stewart

OST ORCHID BOOKS published today contain colour photographs which show the fascinating diversity of colour and shape among orchid flowers. Francis Bauer's great skill, and the value of his drawings to botanists and orchid lovers nearly two hundred years later, lay in his use of dissecting tools and a microscope to discover and record the minutest details of orchid flowers, even the cells and their nuclei in some cases, with an accuracy and style which have never been surpassed.

This section of the book shows reproductions of ten of Bauer's pages of drawings of dissected orchid flowers and their parts. Four were published in his *Illustrations of Orchidaceous Plants, with Notes and Prefatory Remarks by John Lindley* between 1830 and 1838 and six are published here for the first time. Lindley used his collaboration with Bauer to publish an essay summarizing his own observations of orchid structure and function linked with a classification of the various genera into tribes. His recognition of several major groups according to the type of pollen and its arrangement on the column was fundamental and is still the basis of orchid classification today.

The drawings of *Broughtonia sanguinea* on page 21 have not been published before. They illustrate the basic structures – three sepals, two petals and a lip (or labellum) surrounding the central column – which are present in every orchid flower however modified or reduced it may be.

The next three pages of drawings refer to the function of the reproductive parts of an orchid flower: a group of pollinia squashed in water to reveal thousands of pollen grains; sections of the ovary showing many immature ovules on three Y-shaped placentae; and the mature fruit and seeds which result from a successful pollination. From Lindley's remarks it is clear that he and Robert Brown, Sir Joseph Banks's librarian, did not accept Bauer's theory of the function of the pollen and stigma in orchid flowers. Brown's interpretation proved correct, but Lindley pointed out that this 'does not diminish the value of Mr. Bauer's observations'.

Finally, there are six pages of illustrations which reveal some of the diversity of column structure in the *Orchidaceae*. They have been chosen to show the features which Lindley thought were significant and which are the basis for recognizing six subfamilies in modern classifications such as that of Dressler (1981). Cribb (in Bechtel, Cribb and Launert, 1992) followed a more recent proposal by Dressler (1983) to unite the *Epidendroideae* and *Vandoideae* although together they make a very large and diverse subfamily. Other authors, including Pridgeon (1992) and Seidenfaden and Wood (1992), maintain the six subfamilies illustrated here.

# THE BASIC STRUCTURE OF AN ORCHID FLOWER

EXAMPLE *Broughtonia sanguinea* (Swartz) R. Brown
(Syn. *Epidendrum sanguineum* Swartz)

The showy parts of an orchid flower are arranged in two whorls, each of three parts. On the outside of the flower are three sepals, one often slightly different from the other two which occupy a lateral position. The inner whorl consists of two similar petals which may be larger or smaller than the sepals or similar to them, and a different, third petal which is usually designated the lip or labellum. This is almost always distinctively different from all the other floral parts, sometimes smaller, but often much larger and more colourful. Because the pedicel is usually twisted through 180°, the labellum is usually placed on the lower side of the flower in a convenient position to provide a landing platform for a visiting insect.

The reproductive parts of the flower lie in its centre and are more or less fused together in a relatively massive structure called the column.

The column is short or long, often winged on either side, sometimes differently coloured, and has direct connection with the ovary which is below the flower. In the majority of the orchids the single anther lies at or near the apex of the column. The anther conceals the pollen, usually aggregated into pollinia within the cells of a thin-walled anther cap, and has a very short, fragile filament attaching it to the column. In *Broughtonia* there are four pollinia under the white anther cap. The stigma is usually a simple, hollow cavity on the inner or lower side of the column.

*Broughtonia* is distinguished from other genera in the subfamily *Epidendroideae* by the long spur at the base of the sepals which is adnate to the ovary. It forms a nectary attractive to butterflies which pollinate the flowers of this species in Jamaica.

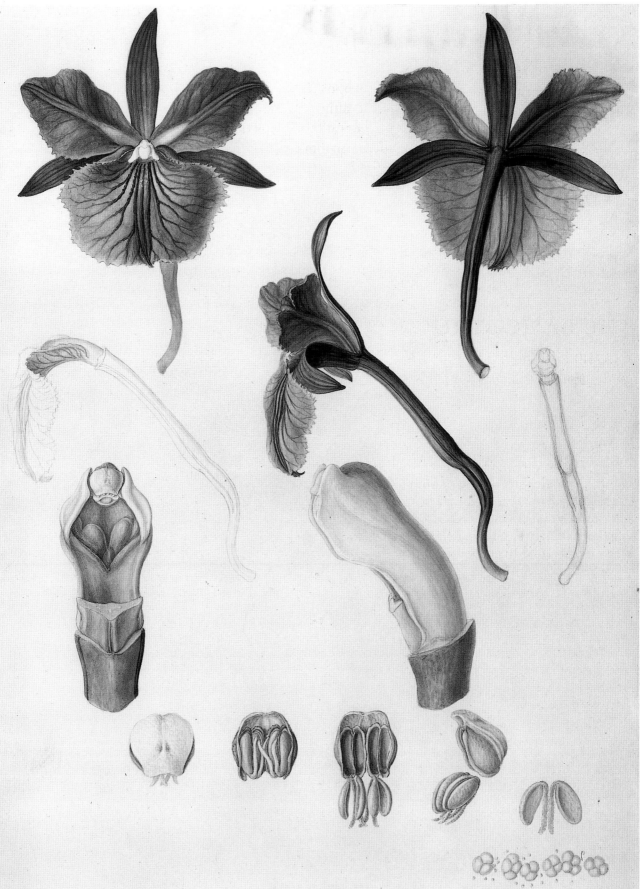

"August 9th 1802
Mr Barret at Ewel."

Broughtonia sanguinea, Brown. C.H.K.
Epidendrum sanguineum. Swartz. prodr.
Dendrobium sanguineum. W.

# THE FUNCTION OF AN ORCHID FLOWER
## I The anther and pollinia

EXAMPLE *Bletia purpurea* (Lamarck) De Candolle (*see* colour plate on page 152)

# THE FUNCTION OF AN ORCHID FLOWER
## II The ovary

EXAMPLE *Bletia purpurea* (Lamarck) De Candolle (*opposite*)

The single anther of a *Bletia* flower contains two sets of four pollinia. They are yellow and hard, somewhat compressed into the anther cells while still in the flower.

To show the real nature of the waxy pollinia of this and other orchid flowers, Bauer removed one set of four pollinia from a flower and immersed it in water. The individual pollen grains, and the way they cohere together in masses, then became visible under the microscope. The elastic tissue uniting the individual pollinia appears as a web of material with more pollen grains scattered among it.

Bauer patiently sketched several thousand pollen grains at a magnification of 100 times and one group of four and a few separate pollen grains at 400 times. The sketches were made in 1801; this illustration was published in part in 1830.

As in *Narcissus, Iris* and other familiar monocotyledonous genera, the ovary of an orchid is below the flower. In many orchids it only develops fully after pollination and is slender and little different from the pedicel at flowering time. Dissections such as those that Bauer made reveal that the ovary is made up of three carpels. In most orchids, including *Bletia*, there are no walls between the carpels, and the whole of the centre of the ovary contains the developing ovules. They are borne on Y-shaped placentae which are outgrowths of the ovary wall. In a few primitive orchids (including *Apostasia, see* page 26) the ovary has three separate cells.

The two drawings on the opposite page were made in 1801; they show a longitudinal and a transverse section of the ovary of *Bletia purpurea* drawn at a magnification of 60 times. They were published as separate plates in *Illustrations of Orchidaceous Plants* in 1830.

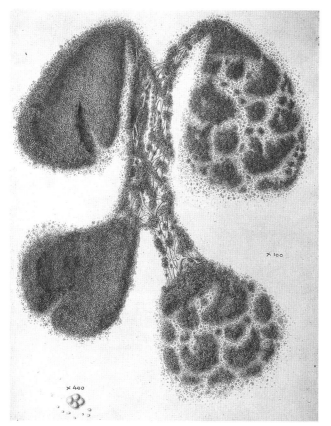

A

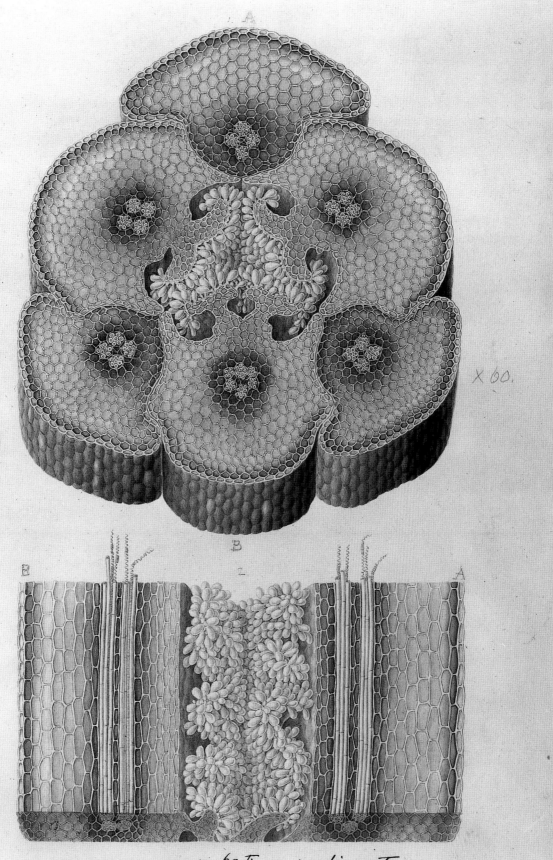

B

B                                                    2                                                    A

× 60.

× 60 times in diameter.

Bletia
Limodorum altum

# THE FUNCTION OF AN ORCHID FLOWER
## III The fruit and seeds

EXAMPLE *Epipactis palustris* (Linnaeus) Crantz

After pollination the ovary rapidly expands, firstly while the ovules grow in readiness for fertilization, and secondly while the seeds develop to maturity. After a period of weeks or months the wall of the ovary dries out, turns brown and splits along three or six of its valves, or rarely along only one ventral suture. The seeds are released into the air and disseminated by wind. Under the microscope the tiny embryo is visible as a dark spherical or ovoid shape enclosed within the network of the seed coat. The seed coat has a small opening where it was attached to the ovary wall and through which a fungal hypha may eventually reach the embryo to promote germination.

The prodigality of tiny orchid seeds is a source of wonder to anyone who has examined a ripe capsule. Bauer closely examined and drew the capsules of many species and drew their seeds at a magnification of 100 times. These drawings of *Epipactis palustris* were prepared in October 1799 but have not been published until now. The drawings of a capsule and seed at the top of the plate, made at the same time, are of *Cypripedium calceolus*.

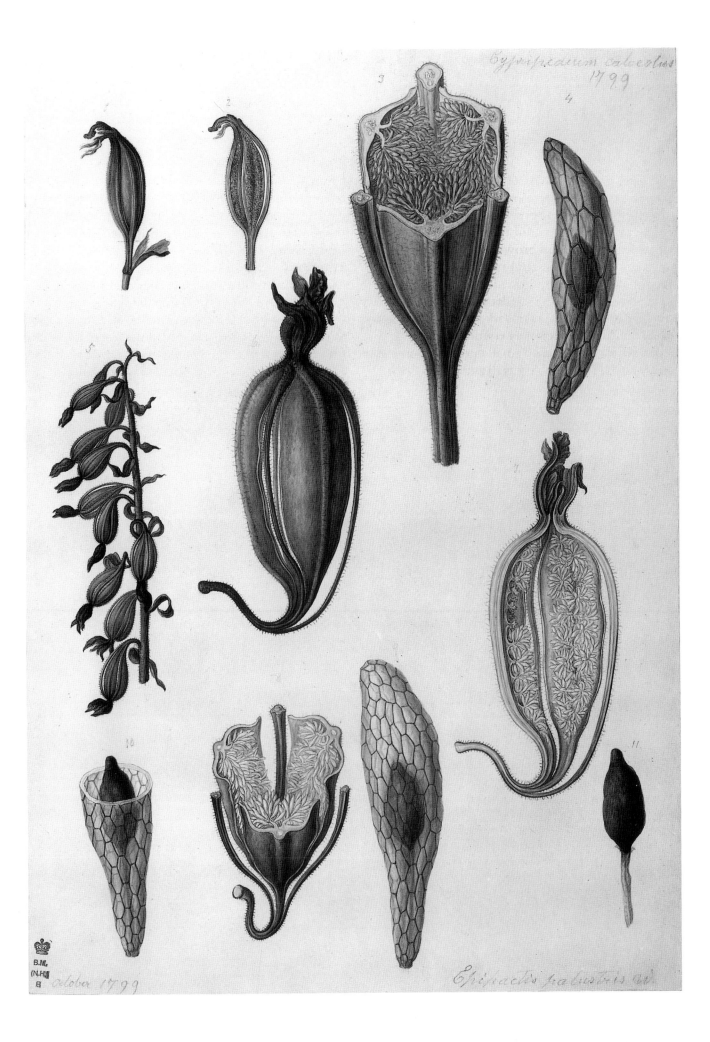

Cypripedium calceolus
1799

aloba 1799

Epipactis palustris Web

# THE STRUCTURE OF ORCHID FLOWERS AND CLASSIFICATION  I *Apostasioideae*

EXAMPLE  *Apostasia nuda* R. Brown and *Apostasia wallichii* R. Brown

Sometimes treated as members of a different family, the *Apostasiaceae*, the two genera and about fifteen species of this subfamily occur in tropical Asia and have small flowers which are superficially somewhat lily-like. In Bauer's illustration the bud at the top left has been opened and dissected to show the three sepals and three petals. The third petal is slightly narrower than the other two especially at its base. A bigger difference from other orchid flowers lies in the structure of the column: it supports two large stamens in which the anthers are free and the filaments are united with the central style only at the base. The stigma and style, and the enlarged drawing of a single anther, show further similarities to other monocotyledonous flowers. The second genus in this subfamily, *Neuwiedia*, is even more different from other orchids in having three similar stamens instead of two. At the bottom of the plate the drawings show that in two species of *Apostasia* the ovary is three-celled, and the seeds of both species have a thickened coat somewhat like the seeds of *Vanilla*.

Bauer made sketches of these two species from dried material in 1832. The lithograph by M. Gauci, which was published in *Illustrations of Orchidaceous Plants* in the same year, greatly enhances the original pencil sketches.

TAB. 15.                    FRUCTIFICATION.

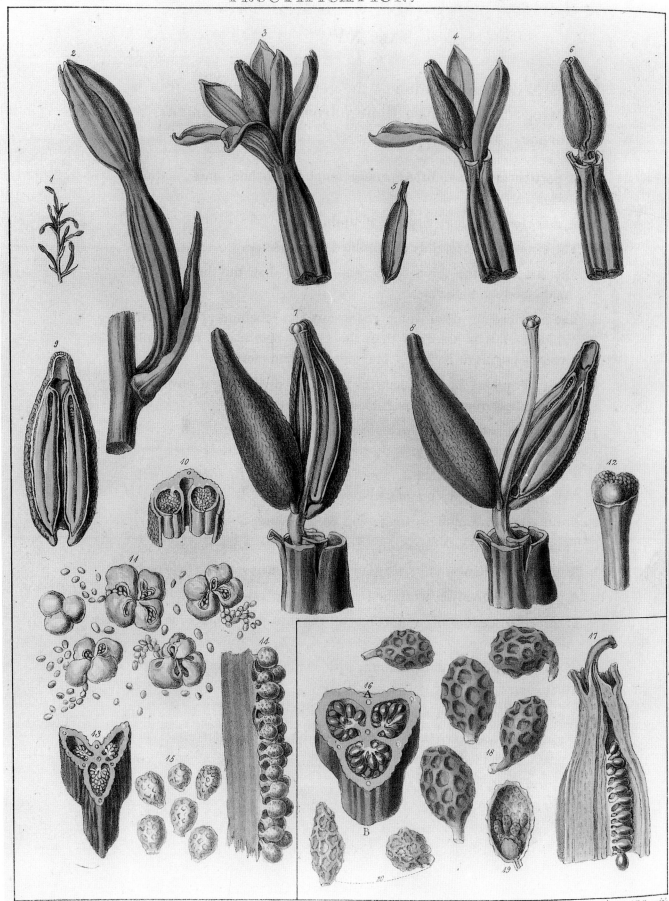

Franz Bauer del. 1832            Gauci lithog            Printed by C. Hullmandel.

# THE STRUCTURE OF ORCHID FLOWERS
## AND CLASSIFICATION  II *Cypripedioideae*

EXAMPLE *Cypripedium reginae* Walter

The 'slipper orchids' are distinguished from all other subfamilies by the calceolate or slipper-shaped lip. This is balanced by a large dorsal sepal, fused lateral sepals which are often hidden by the lip, and a pair of petals which may be spreading or pendulous in the different species. There are only four genera, *Cypripedium*, whose species are distributed throughout the north temperate region, *Paphiopedilum* in Asia, *Phragmipedium* in Central and South America and *Selenipedium* in tropical South America.

Bauer's drawings of several species of *Cypri-pedium* are reproduced in colour on pages 63–73 of this book and several of them show the very distinctive column of this subfamily. It is short with two lateral, fertile anthers and a third, sterile anther which has become modified to form a shield-shaped staminode. The stigma is shortly stalked, hidden below the staminode in the open flower, and its hairy surface is faintly divided into three areas.

Bauer made his drawings of this species from a living plant in Lady Banks's garden in 1798 and 1802.

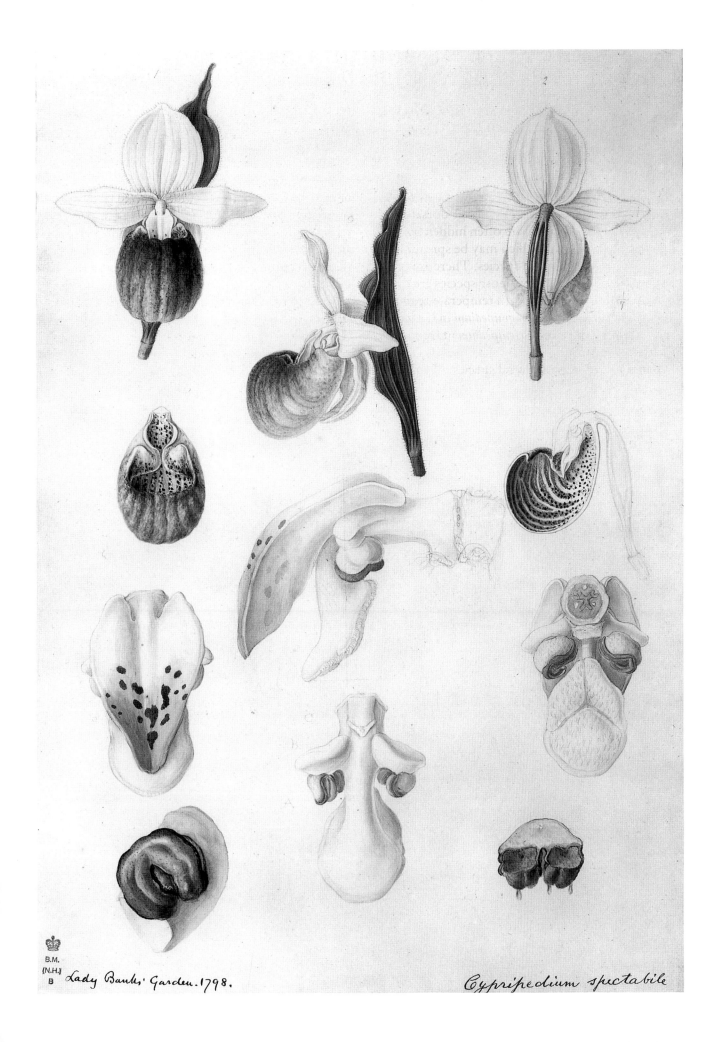

Lady Banks' Garden. 1798.

Cypripedium spectabile

# THE STRUCTURE OF ORCHID FLOWERS
## AND CLASSIFICATION  III *Orchidoideae*

EXAMPLE *Platanthera chlorantha* (Custer) Reichenbach filius
(Syn. *Habenaria chlorantha* (Custer) Babington)

The *Orchidoideae* comprise many of the most familiar orchid genera of Europe, North America, Australia and South Africa. They are terrestrial plants which reappear each spring from a pair of underground tubers or tuberoids. The column is usually short and erect and the anther is firmly united with the column at its base. There is a single anther with two cells, each containing a single pollinium. The cells are often parallel or may be widely separated as they are in *Platanthera chlorantha*, shown in the drawings on the opposite page. Each pollinium bears a mass of rather mealy pollen which is aggregated into packets called 'massulae' on a long slender caudicle above the sticky viscidium. The drawings of this species were prepared in May and June 1801; they have not been published until now.

HABENARIA.

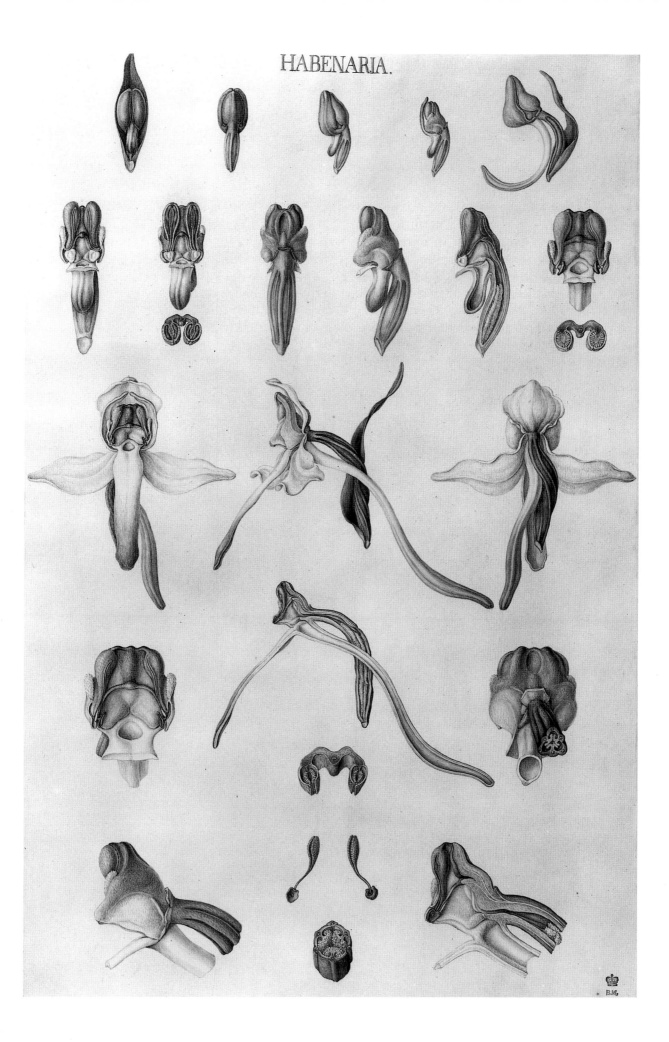

# THE STRUCTURE OF ORCHID FLOWERS
# AND CLASSIFICATION IV *Spiranthoideae*

EXAMPLE *Stenorrhynchos speciosum* (Jacquin) L. C. Richard
(Syn. *Spiranthes speciosa* (Jacquin) A. Richard

This is a group of mainly tropical terrestrial orchids which perennate by creeping rhizomes rather than tubers. The flowers are mostly small but quite distinctive in their column structure. Bauer drew the flower and large supporting bract of *Stenorrhynchos speciosum* at a magnification of 8 times. Below the front and side view of the flowers, the drawings of the column clearly show the single anther on the upper side of the column. The two pairs of pollinia, one pair from each anther cell, are shown in front and rear view at the bottom of the plate. The four pollinia are attached to a single viscidium which, in the open flower, lies at the extreme apex of the column. The stigma lies on the lower side of the beaked column.

These drawings were made in 1794 from a plant at Kew Gardens. A plate prepared from them and others made at the same time was published in Bauer's *Illustrations of Orchidaceous Plants* in 1834.

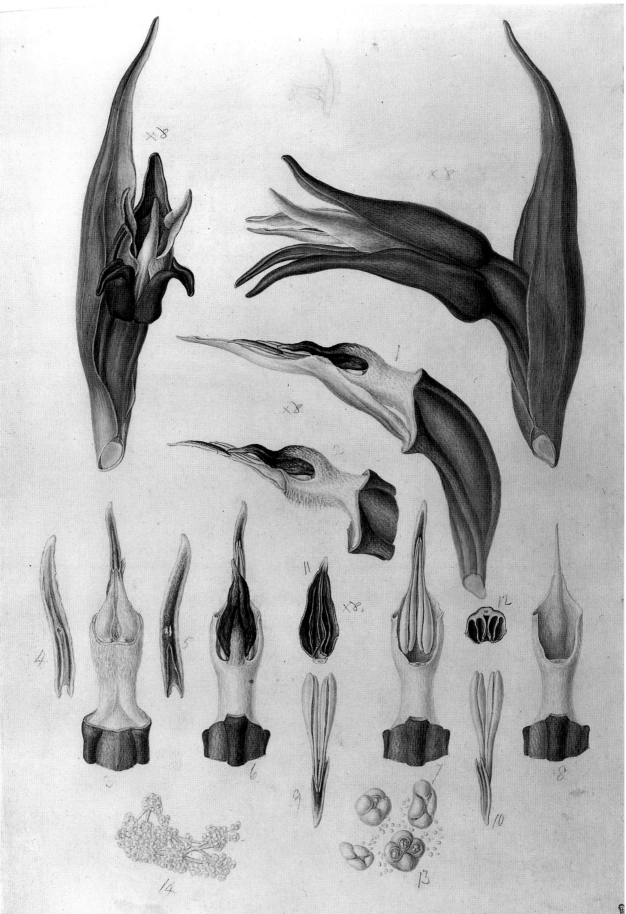

1794

*Neottia speciosa*

# THE STRUCTURE OF ORCHID FLOWERS
# AND CLASSIFICATION  V *Epidendroideae*

EXAMPLE *Epidendrum elongatum* Jacquin

More than half of all orchid species are grouped in this one large and diverse subfamily. The character which ties them together is the anther which is erect in the young flower bud, but as the bud develops it bends down over the axis of the column until, in the open flower, it is held at right angles to the axis of the column. The anther has two, four or eight cells each holding a single pollinium. There is no viscidium in *Epidendrum* but in several genera of the subfamily this structure is well developed. The stigma lies on the ventral side of the column, well separated from the anther.

These drawings were made in June 1802 and have not been published previously.

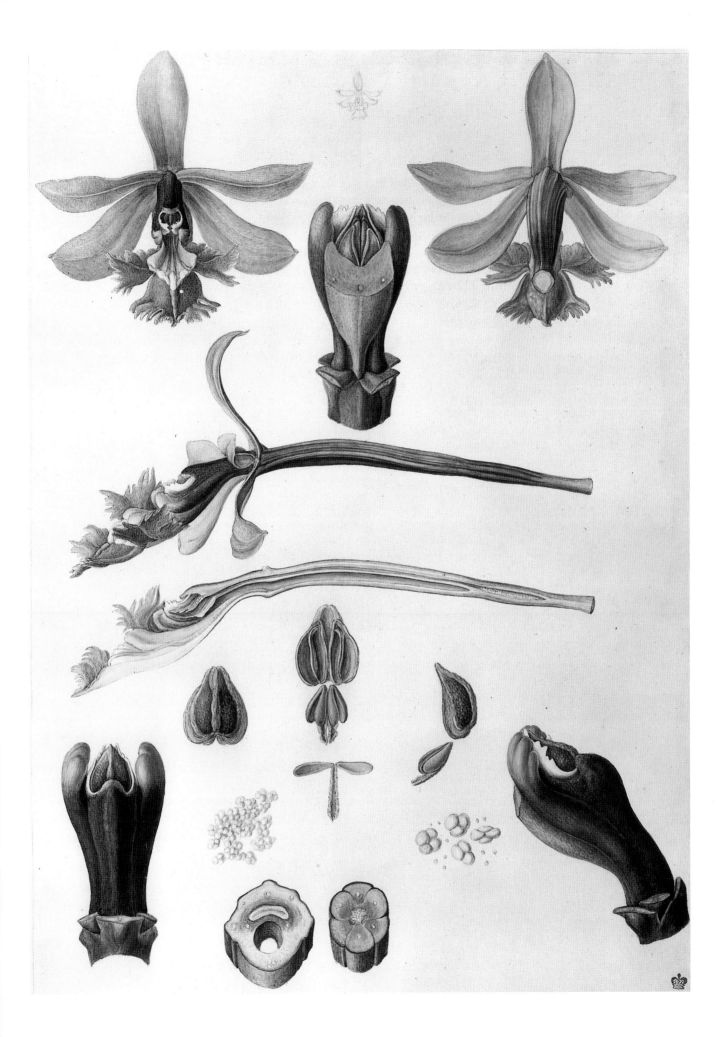

# THE STRUCTURE OF ORCHID FLOWERS AND CLASSIFICATION   VI *Vandoideae*

EXAMPLE   *Vanda tessellata* (Roxburgh) G. Don
(Syn. *Epidendrum tessellatum* Roxburgh)

Traditionally regarded as the most highly evolved orchids, the members of this subfamily are mainly epiphytes and are distributed throughout the tropical regions of the world. The flowers have a short column with the pollinia hidden under a removable anther cap at its apex. The stigma is a sticky cavity immediately below the rostellum which supports the viscidium. The pollinarium bears two waxy pollinia attached by a short stipe to the viscidium. Within the subfamily there are genera with one or two pairs of pollinia, each with a separate stipe or with fused stipes and each with a separate viscidium or sharing a single viscidium. Many genera can be recognized immediately by the characters of the pollinia, even when these have been collected from insects.

Sir Joseph Banks flowered this *Vanda* for the first time in England in 1819 at Spring Grove, Isleworth, not far from Kew Green where Francis Bauer lived. It is one of the Asiatic orchids with a monopodial growth habit. The drawing of *Aerides odorata*, also published for the first time in this book (page 41), shows the distinctive habit of these orchids.

Further reading – *see* page 155

October 1st 1820

Lady Banks

Vanda tesselata

# A selection of
# Franz Bauer's orchid paintings

*by* Joyce Stewart and William T. Stearn

DURING THE PERIOD 1830–38, twenty-eight of Franz Bauer's orchid paintings were published as *Illustrations of Orchidaceous Plants; with Notes and prefatory Remarks by John Lindley*. The original plates for this work are in the collection at the Natural History Museum, London. From these we have selected *Cleisostoma paniculatum*, *Oncidium baueri* and *Satyrium erectum* for reproduction here.

In Göttingen we studied two volumes of Bauer's orchid paintings preserved in the Niedersächsische Staats- und Universitätsbibliothek. MS 94 Band XII contains thirteen plates of European orchids which appear to be copies from Jacquin's five-volume work, *Flora Austriacae*, and sixteen plates of American orchids which appear to be copies of plates in Jacquin's *Selectarum Stirpium Americanarum Historia*. We have reproduced the illustrations of *Himantoglossum hircinum*, *Limodorum abortivum*, *Maxillaria coccinea* and *Orchis purpurea* from this volume. MS 94 Band XIII contains twenty-two pages of coloured drawings, all of Australian orchids. These plates were prepared from specimens collected for Sir Joseph Banks near Port Jackson (now Sydney) by William Paterson between 1791 and 1810. We have selected five of these illustrations which include the orchids *Caladenia caerulea*, *Dendrobium linguiforme*, *D. speciosum*, *Dipodium punctatum*, *Diuris aurea*, *D. sulphurea* and *Glossodia major*.

At the Natural History Museum there are illustrations of almost all of the 113 species of orchids listed by Robert Brown in the second edition of Aiton's *Hortus Kewensis* (1813) and of other species which came into the Royal Gardens at Kew later. There are many sketches of parts of plants and flowers and unfinished drawings as well as the beautifully composed studies of British and American orchids. These may have been intended for publication.

From these we have chosen a selection which shows Franz Bauer's skill with the pencil and paintbrush in illustrating what he studied at its natural size and at considerable magnification. The drawings also demonstrate the development and refinement of his style from the first copies he made for Baron Nicolaus von Jacquin before he left Austria in 1788 to the detailed records of the life histories of European orchids which he made in his middle years at Kew. These were followed by portrayals of new introductions from the tropics as they came into flower in the Royal Gardens.

## *Aerides odorata* Loureiro

COMMON NAME  fox tail orchid
DISTRIBUTION  widespread in Asia, from tropical Himalayas of Sikkim, Nepal and India, south China, Malaysia, Thailand and elsewhere in southeast Asia to the Philippines

This is the type species of the genus *Aerides*, described by the Portuguese missionary and naturalist João Loureiro in 1790. The generic name combines the Greek words *aer* – 'air', and *eides* – 'resembling', in allusion to these epiphytic plants apparently deriving their nourishment from the air. They usually have extensive roots projecting in all directions as well as attached to the substratum.

Sir Joseph Banks, who had received plants from China, gave this orchid to the Royal Gardens at Kew in 1800. The plant Bauer illustrated was a later introduction which he labelled '*Aerides cornutum* Roxbg. India'. William Roxburgh, a Scottish botanist and physician, who was Superintendent of the Calcutta Botanic Garden from 1793 to 1813, sent a large number of plants to Kew. John Lindley adopted the epithet *cornutum* in the *Botanical Register* (t. 1485) in 1832. He wrote ecstatically about the great mass of blossoms this species produced and was enthralled by their curious form, delicate colour and delicious perfume.

Now that the wide distribution and variability of *A. odorata* has become apparent, the name *A. cornuta*, given to plants of Indian origin, is treated as a synonym.

## *Aceras anthropophorum* (Linnaeus) Aiton filius

COMMON NAME   man orchid
DISTRIBUTION   Europe and north Africa

The flower of the man orchid has the sepals and petals arranged to look like a pale green head, while the lip resembles the trunk of the man with its four lobes spread out in the positions of arms and legs. There is a faint scent of coumarin which attracts small insects who crawl up into the upper parts of the flower.

The man orchid is still quite common in undisturbed vegetation on calcareous soils. It occurs in grassland and woodland margins but is often overlooked because it is not very conspicuous. In eastern Europe, especially in Turkey and southern Greece, it is now much less common than formerly Many sites from which it has disappeared have been cultivated or built over, but there are other places where it has reappeared in land that has been neglected after a period of cultivation.

The generic name *Aceras* is derived from the Greek *a* – 'without' and *keras* – 'horn', hence 'spur', referring to the lack of a spur-like projection in the flower. *Anthropophorum*, from *anthropos* – 'man', *phoros* – 'bearing', refers to the shape of the flower.

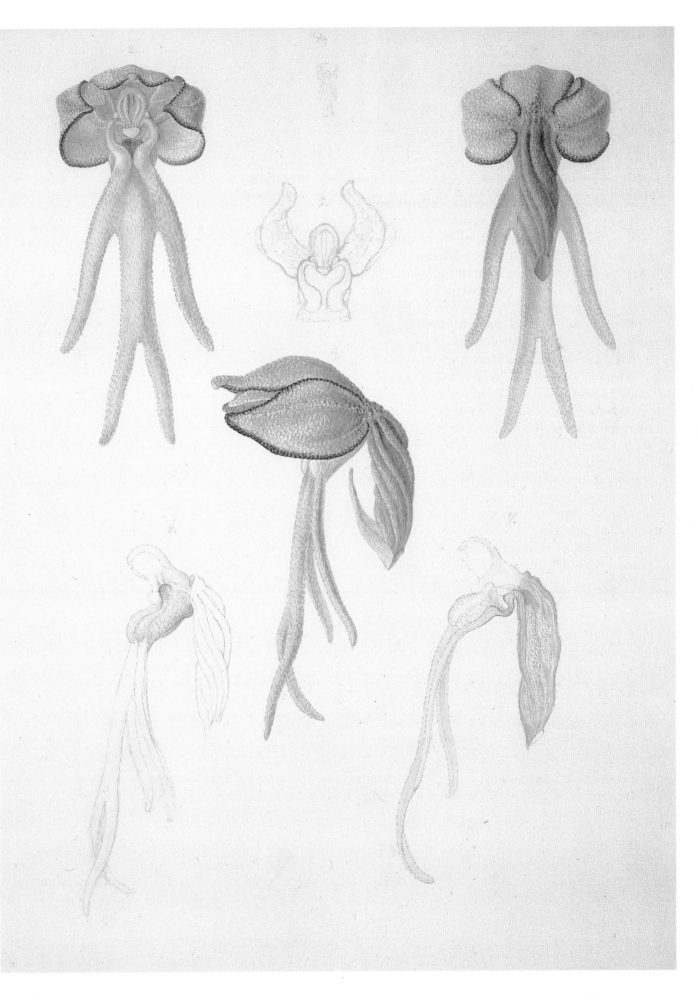

# *Anacamptis pyramidalis* (Linnaeus) Richard

COMMON NAME  pyramidal orchid
DISTRIBUTION  widespread over southern and central Europe, north Africa and central Asia

The name of this genus is derived from the Greek word, *anakampto* – 'to bend back', which presumably refers to the shape of the slender spur at the base of the lip. It contains no free nectar, but plant sap becomes available to visiting insects who break apart the cells lining the inner surface of the spur. The pyramidal shape of the inflorescence is quite unmistakable. The flowers vary in colour on different plants from white, pale or dark pink to a rich magenta.

The flower is shaped so that it can only be pollinated by butterflies. The lip has two upright ridges or folds which guide the insect's slender proboscis as if through a tunnel, straight down into the nectary. The pollinia are held in a pouch above the entrance to the spur and are attached to a single sticky disc which is saddle-shaped. This disc attaches itself to the proboscis as it is withdrawn from the spur. The pollinia fall forwards as the butterfly moves to another flower, or even another plant, so that they are in the right position to effect pollination at the next visit. Bauer has revealed all these details in his drawings dated 26 June 1811.

Plants are easily located in well-drained or dry situations in open grassland, on the downs, roadsides, and even on golf courses. It is one of those species which seems to thrive where competition is not too great. Plants survive well in areas where the grass is cropped regularly, by grazing or for hay. This species also colonizes new grassland and is frequently found at the edge of calcareous sand dunes.

44

Anacamptis (Richard)
Orchis pyramidalis W.

# *Bonatea speciosa* (Linnaeus filius) Willdenow

DISTRIBUTION South Africa

The younger Linnaeus described this terrestrial orchid from a specimen in a collection of Cape plants made by the Swedish botanist, Carl Peter Thunberg. In 1805 the epithet *speciosa* – 'showy' was transferred to the new genus *Bonatea* by the German botanist Willdenow who named it in honour of Giuseppe Antonio Bonato (1753–1836), Professor of Botany at Padua in Italy. The genus now comprises about twenty species in Africa and Arabia. With their rather fleshy leaves and green and white flowers the plants of this genus resemble those of the large genus *Habenaria*. The flowers differ in the attachment of the lip, lower petal lobes and lateral sepals to the stigmatic arms.

All the species of *Bonatea* are tuberous terrestrial orchids. They are fairly easy to maintain in cultivation provided the sandy soil in which they grow is kept completely dry during the resting season. The showy *Bonatea*, *B. speciosa*, is recorded from near sea level to over 1,200 m in various parts of South Africa where, depending on the locality, it flowers from June to February.

Bauer illustrated this orchid in May 1824. William Aiton sent a division of the Kew plant to the Royal Botanic Garden, Edinburgh and in 1826 it was illustrated there for *Curtis's Botanical Magazine* (t. 2926).

Francis Bauer del;
May 1824.

# *Brassavola cucullata* (Linnaeus) R. Brown

DISTRIBUTION   Mexico to Honduras, the West Indies
and northern South America

This species of *Brassavola* has longer and narrower leaves than the much better known 'alluring lady of the night', *B. nodosa* (Linnaeus) Lindley. Like that species it is very sweetly scented at night, emitting a distinct 'white floral' scent during the hours that moths are abroad.

It was first described by Linnaeus in the second edition of his *Species Plantarum* (1763) as *Epidendrum cucullatum*. Robert Brown made it the type of his new genus *Brassavola* in 1813 when he described the plants then growing at Kew for the second edition of Aiton's *Hortus Kewensis*. It seems likely that Bauer drew and painted the same plant that Robert Brown saw. Although his illustration is not dated, he records that the specimen came from the West Indies. Vice Admiral William Bligh brought plants to Kew in 1793 after his successful introduction of breadfruit to the West Indies in HMS Providence.

The genus is named in honour of an Italian physician and botanist Antonio Musa Brasavola (*sic*) (1500–55), who was Professor of Medicine at Ferrara in Italy. About fifteen species are now recognized, all occurring in tropical America.

## *Brassia maculata* R. Brown

COMMON NAME  spider orchid (in West Indies)
DISTRIBUTION  Guatemala, Belize, Honduras
and the West Indies

This attractive species is today considered rather rare. It was introduced to Kew by Sir Joseph Banks in 1806 and flowered there on several occasions. Robert Brown was Banks's botanist and librarian; this species was unique in his new genus, *Brassia*, at the time it was described in 1813. The name commemorates William Brass (d. 1783), originally a gardener employed by the first Duke of Northumberland who went to West Africa in 1780 to collect plants for Banks and a syndicate of friends.

Other species were added to this genus throughout the nineteenth century and about twenty-five are now recognized. All the species of *Brassia* have a distinctive and similar scent which has been described as 'evoking a fern–covered heath and the resinoid secretion of *Cistus* species'. They are easy to grow in a well-drained compost in intermediate glasshouse conditions.

Brassia maculata

# Catasetum macrocarpum L.C. Richard ex Kunth

COMMON NAMES   monkshead, monkey goblet (in Trinidad)
DISTRIBUTION   Trinidad, Guyana, Venezuela and Brazil

The name *Catasetum*, from the Greek word *kata* – 'down' and the Latin *seta* – 'bristle', refers to the two appendages, like antennae, which are at the base of the column in male flowers. One or both of them is easily touched by a visiting insect, usually a bee, trying to reach the spicy scent which is concentrated at the base of the column. The movement of the antenna releases a trigger mechanism which ensures that the entire pollinarium is hurled on to the back of the bee. It becomes firmly stuck on immediately. By the time the bee enters a female flower, usually on another plant, the anther cap has fallen off and the stipe holds the pollinarium in such a way that it is easily deposited on the stigmatic surface.

*Catasetum* is one of the few orchid genera which produces flowers of two or three different kinds. When plants of this genus were first discovered this curious characteristic was not understood. Plants with female flowers and a few which produced hermaphrodite flowers were described in different genera from those with the male flowers which had the extraordinary antennae. It was Charles Darwin who investigated all these, obtaining flowers from his friend Joseph Hooker at Kew and demonstrating that they all belonged to the same genus, and in some cases to a single species.

## *Cleisostoma paniculatum* (Ker Gawler) Garay

DISTRIBUTION   China, including Hong Kong and Taiwan

*Cleisostoma* is a large genus of monopodial orchids, usually epiphytes, with small flowers. Some eighty to a hundred species are distributed throughout mainland Asia and adjacent islands as far south as Australia and the Pacific. The name refers to the blocking of the entrance to the spur by a large callus (from the Greek *kleistos* – 'closed' and *stoma* – 'mouth').

This species was placed by John Lindley in the genus *Sarcanthus* when he published this illustration in Bauer's *Illustrations of Orchidaceous Plants*. It had already been described as Sir Joseph Banks's *Aerides* by John Bellenden Ker (né Gawler) in 1817 (*Botanical Register*, t. 220) and transferred to *Vanda* by Robert Brown in 1820. The short, fleshy lip has a curious pair of outgrowths resembling horns at its apex.

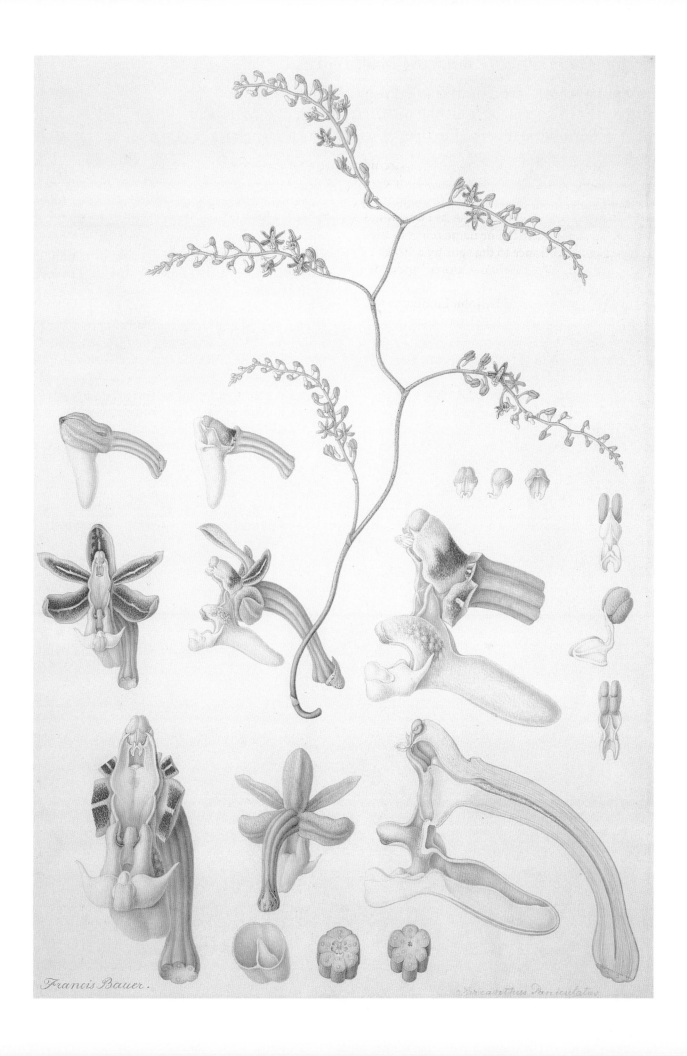

Francis Bauer.

Arpanthus Paniculatus

# *Coeloglossum viride* (Linnaeus) Hartman

COMMON NAME  frog orchid
DISTRIBUTION  throughout the northern temperate regions of
the northern hemisphere, Europe, Asia and north America

This somewhat inconspicuous orchid is rather variable in colour, often heavily shaded with brown or purplish red, while the typical forms have a pale green lip with red or brown on the ovary and at the base of the flower. It grows on grassy banks and in areas where grassland is being invaded by scrub, but can also be found in coniferous or deciduous woods. In Asia it extends up to 4,000 m above sea level. It is usually found on calcareous soils, but is not confined to them, being well known on moorlands which may be quite acid.

The flower structure of this, the only species of the genus, is unique: the elongated lip is three-lobed at the apex and from the central lobe a band of thickened tissue extends up to the nectary which is a short bulbous spur. Two small cavities on either side contain small amounts of nectar, a taste of more to come. The spur has a narrow entrance immediately below the stigmatic surface. Darwin postulated that a visiting insect would spend time feeding at the base of the lip before seeking this entrance so that pollinia it was carrying from another flower would dry and tip forward to the right position to strike the stigma. Despite, or perhaps because of, this device, seeds are easily set and plants are often found in fruit very soon after flowering. The generic name comes from the Greek *koilos* – 'hollow', and *glossa* – 'tongue'.

# Cymbidium aloifolium (Linnaeus) Swartz

DISTRIBUTION   widespread in southeast Asia, recorded in Sri Lanka, India, Sikkim, Nepal, South China, Hong Kong, Cambodia, Vietnam, Laos, Thailand, West Malaysia, Java and Burma

*Cymbidium* hybrids are commonly cultivated and grown as conservatory and house plants in many parts of the world. The wild species from which they have been derived, after more than a hundred years of breeding, are much less frequently grown.

*Cymbidium aloifolium*, one of the first to be seen in Europe, is the type of the genus. It was illustrated by H. A. van Rheede tot Draakestein, the Governor of Malabar, at the beginning of the eighteenth century. His *Hortus Indicus Malabaricus* is one of the most celebrated of early floras, published in Amsterdam during the period 1678–1703. Linnaeus cited this illustration when he described it as *Epidendrum aloifolium* in his *Species Plantarum* in 1753. Thus the species became one of the first epiphytic orchids named in the Linnaean binomial system of nomenclature. The Swedish botanist Olof Swartz transferred the species to *Cymbidium* when he established the genus in 1799. This was in fact his type for the new genus. Bauer's drawing was made only two years later, in August 1801. Plants had been introduced to Kew as early as 1789 by the nurseryman Conrad Loddiges.

This *Cymbidium*, one of the lowland species in southeast Asia, has thick leaves and is able to withstand hot dry conditions in rather open forests. It grows in the large forks of tree trunks and the hollows of large branches. Plants flower during the rainy season, often in April, and can even survive on isolated trees that remain in the fields and near houses when the forest has been removed.

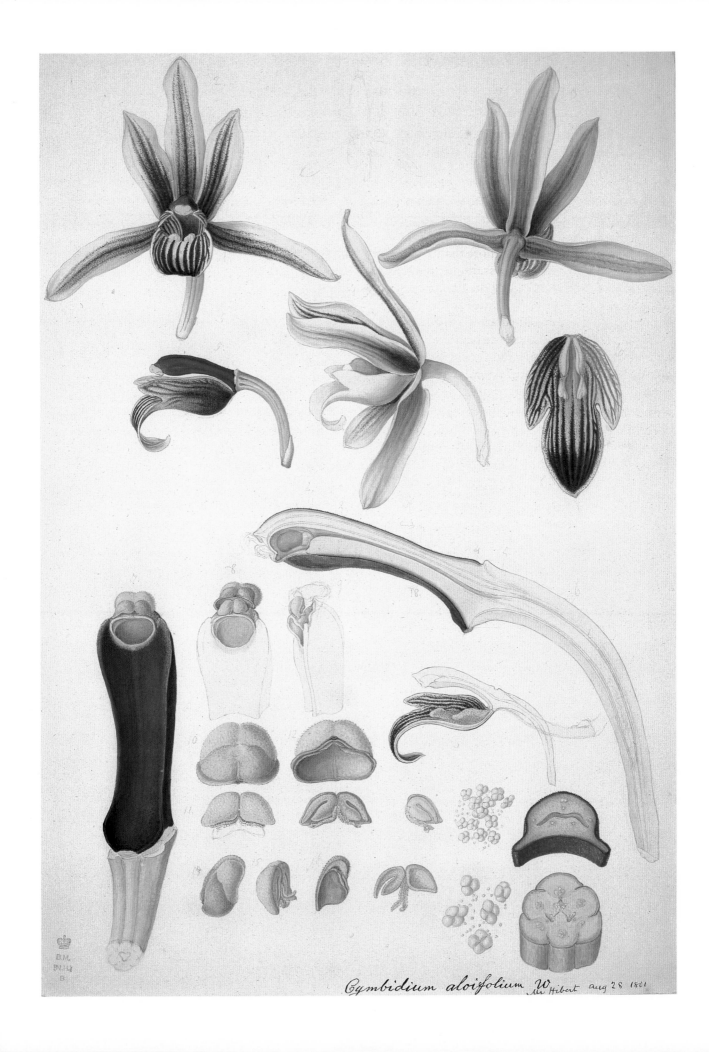

*Cymbidium aloifolium* 20 Aug 28 1801
Mr Hibert

# Cymbidium ensifolium (Linnaeus) Swartz

DISTRIBUTION    widely distributed in southeast Asia, Sri Lanka, India, China, Hong Kong, Taiwan, Ryukyu Islands, Indo-China, Thailand, Malaysia, Sumatra, Java, Borneo, New Guinea and the Philippines

This species became known to Linnaeus from a specimen acquired in Canton by the Swedish botanist and missionary Pehr Osbeck. He noted that it was cultivated in Chinese houses for its scent. Never widely grown in Europe or America, it has been cultivated in China and Japan for more than two thousand years. There are many named varieties which are recognized horticulturally by small differences in their leaves and flowers. The pale green or cream flowers of those which lack reddish pigments are highly prized as are those with variegated foliage. An albino variant with up to thirteen flowers on its spike is reputed to have had a beneficial effect on the beautiful wife of the Emperor Shi-kotei during the Ch'in Dynasty (249–207 BC). The story is that she had been unable to bear children. The Emperor acquired a plant of this beautiful *Cymbidium* which emitted a delightful fragrance when it flowered in her room the following autumn. As a result, she later produced a son and then twelve more sons, all brave and wise, at annual intervals.

In the wild this species is a terrestrial plant, growing in lightly shaded places in damp situations, often near a stream or in a water-seepage area. It is not easily over-watered in cultivation and usually flowers in the late summer or autumn. It was one of the first Chinese orchids to grow and flower at Kew, the first plants being presented by Dr John Fothergill before 1780.

# *Cypripedium acaule* Aiton

COMMON NAMES  pink lady's slipper, pink moccasin flower
DISTRIBUTION  North America, Canada
and the eastern United States

This species was first named in the *Hortus Kewensis* published under the name of the Kew gardener William Aiton although the work was written by Banks's librarians Solander and Dryander. Aiton probably received it from William Hamilton, Professor of Botany at Glasgow in 1781–90. It is the most common North American lady's slipper orchid and grows in both dry and boggy situations, in woods and out in the open.

It is immediately recognized by its soft, rather hairy leaves, two of which come through the leaf litter early in the spring. As they enlarge in size, the bud begins to emerge between them. The mature plant thus consists simply of a pair of basal leaves and a solitary flower. Well-established plants may produce a number of separate shoots so that a group of flowers appear together.

Though it has long been famous for its pink colour, the greatly enlarged and somewhat grotesque lip of the flower is in fact rather variable. Some forms are known in which the lip is almost red. A white lip accompanied by yellowish green in the other parts of the flower gives the plant a somewhat ghostly appearance on the shady woodland floor. In the south of its range it may be found in flower in April, but further north in the continent flowering is delayed until July.

# *Cypripedium arietinum* R. Brown

COMMON NAME   ram's head lady's slipper
DISTRIBUTION   North America, restricted to the southern parts
of eastern Canada and the extreme north of the United States

The specific epithet of this lady's slipper refers to the fancied resemblance of the flower to a ram's head (from the Latin word *aries* – 'a ram'), with the sepals and petals supplying the ears and horns on either side of the oddly shaped lip.

The name and description were published by Robert Brown in the second edition of Aiton's *Hortus Kewensis* in 1813. It had been introduced to Kew in 1808 by Messrs Chandler and Buckingham. Bauer's painting has a note at the bottom, 'Cyp. arietinum flowered in my own garden May 10 1813'.

This is a rare species in North America today and can be found in two quite different habitats. It grows in the sphagnum bogs that appear in cedar (*Thuja*) woodlands and also in quite dry situations in shallow soil over limestone or sand. It is usually accompanied by other orchid species but none of these occurs in both habitats.

Some botanists place this species in a different genus, *Criosanthes*, because of the curious shape of the lip. There is only one other species with this feature, *C. plectrochilon*, which although remarkably similar is found only in the mountains of southeastern China.

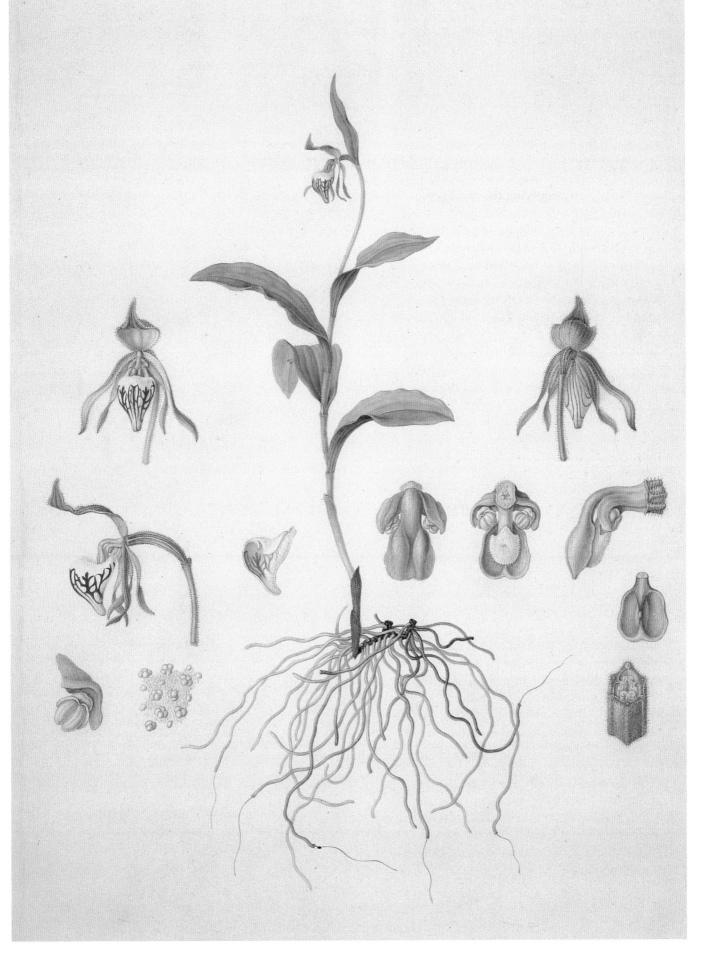

# *Cypripedium calceolus* Linnaeus

COMMON NAME  lady's slipper
DISTRIBUTION   Europe and northern
Asia

The European lady's slipper is one of the most
celebrated of all orchids. Somehow its flowers are
unexpectedly large and showy among other European orchids. Its rarity in modern times has added
to its mystique.

Its vernacular name in German is *Marienschuth*,
latinized as *Calceolus Mariae* by sixteenth-century
herbalists. Linnaeus invented the name *Cypripedium* (from the Greek *Kypris*, a designation of
Aphrodite the goddess of love and beauty supposed to have arisen from the sea near Paphos,
Cyprus, a centre of her worship, and *podion* – 'little
foot'), though he should have used the Greek word
*pedilon* – 'sandal' or 'slipper'. One meaning of the
Greek *pědion* is 'the female genital region',
although it usually means 'a plain'; hence German
scholars, shocked that gardeners might innocently
be using an obscene designation, adopted *pědīlŏn*.
Linnaeus named the genus *Cypripedium* in his *Flora
Lapponica* (1737) and this spelling is the one in use
today. He named the collective species *C. calceolus*
in his *Species Plantarum* (1753), listing as varieties
several other taxa which are now accepted as
distinct species.

The 'sabot de Venus' as it is known in France
and 'lady's slipper' in England has now become a
rare plant, although locally very abundant at places
in Sweden. It is protected by legislation throughout much of its range in Europe. At the Royal
Botanic Gardens, Kew an orchid conservation
project initiated by Sir Robert and Lady Sainsbury
has succeeded in raising young plants from seeds
and establishing some of the seedlings at safe sites
in the wild. There is hope that the sad decline of
populations of this attractive orchid may be
reversed and the misdeeds of gardeners and botanists in the past, who collected so many specimens
from the wild that only one mature plant remains
in England, may be corrected. Late in the 18th
century plants from local woods were sold in the
market place at Settle, Yorkshire. The plant which
Bauer illustrated had been collected for him in
Yorkshire.

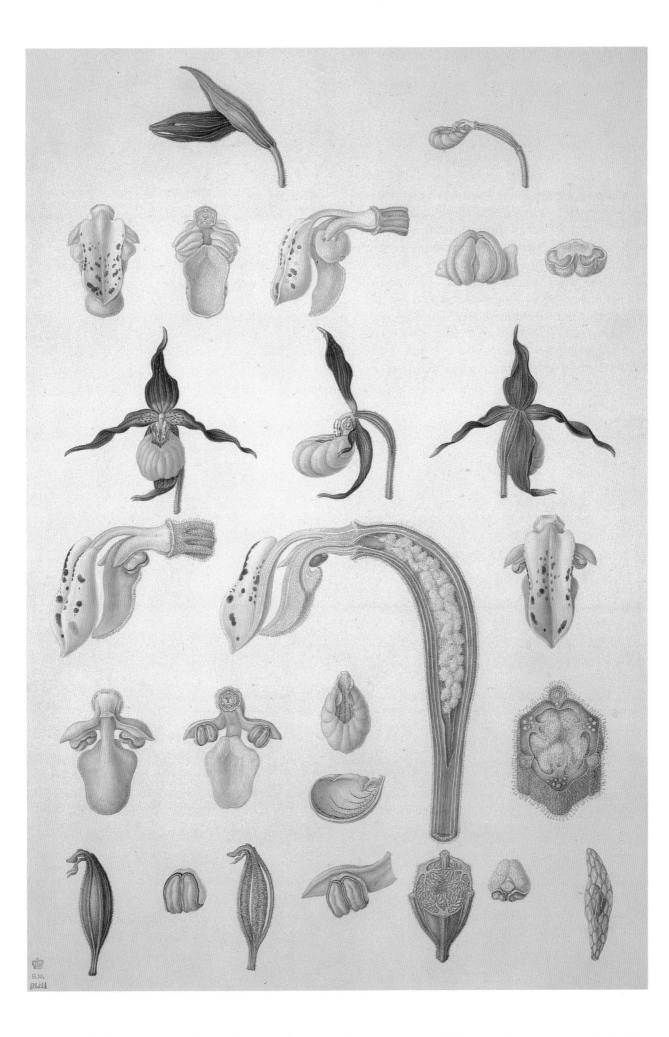

# Cypripedium parviflorum Salisbury

**COMMON NAME** small yellow lady's slipper
**DISTRIBUTION** North America, northeastern United States and the southern parts of eastern Canada

This orchid resembles the European lady's slipper so closely that many people consider that it is only a variety of that species. It is much smaller than the other yellow slipper orchids in North America and is confined to damp boggy habitats in full sunshine. Thus in its habitat, as well as its diminutive size, it is rather different from the European plants, although its coloration is similar. The fragrance which many people have reported of plants in the wild is also characteristic. It was first introduced to cultivation in England in 1759 by Phillip Miller who grew it at Chelsea.

William Jackson Hooker was quite sure of the distinctions between this and the following species, *C. pubescens*, when he described them in *Curtis's Botanical Magazine* in 1830 (t. 3024). He had the opportunity to observe them growing together in a cold frame at the Glasgow Botanic Garden. Well-grown plants are easily recognized as distinct in cultivation, as well as in the wild, but herbarium specimens are much more difficult to identify.

# Cypripedium pubescens Willdenow

COMMON NAMES   yellow moccasin-flower, large yellow lady's slipper
DISTRIBUTION   widespread across Canada and the eastern United
States with additional populations in some southern states

This is the most widely distributed of the American lady's slipper orchids and it has the largest flowers. The sepals and petals are usually yellowish green and paler than the large golden lip, but they may be veined with brownish purple which gives them a reddish tinge. Many variations occur and at least ten distinct varieties have been named. Probably it is most satisfactory to treat it as one rather variable species, though many botanists would consider that it should be treated as a variety of *C. calceolus*.

Flowering time varies with geography, plants in the south flowering as early as April while those in the far north may not produce their blooms until August. Its habitats are as varied as its form. Its ability to thrive on a wide variety of soils, in woods and pastures, shaded and in full sunlight, may account for its remarkable distribution as well as its variety of form. It was first introduced to the Royal Gardens at Kew in 1790 by Sir Joseph Banks.

# *Cypripedium reginae* Walter

**COMMON NAMES** showy lady's slipper, queen lady's slipper
**DISTRIBUTION** North America, southern Canada
from eastern Saskatchewan to Newfoundland
and the northeastern United States

This spectacular orchid was one of the first to be described in a colonial flora. The British-born botanist Thomas Walter published the name and description in his *Flora Caroliniana* in 1788 although it had been mentioned as a variety of *C. calceolus* by Linnaeus in 1753. A year later it was described in Aiton's *Hortus Kewensis* as *C. album*, the white lady's slipper. He recorded that plants had been introduced to Kew about 1770 by William Young. However, the first introduction to English gardens had been much earlier, before 1731 when Philip Miller is known to have been growing plants at Chelsea.

Bauer knew it under yet another synonym, *C. spectabile*, which Salisbury had published in 1791. Bauer noted on a drawing of this species that his specimen came from Lady Banks's garden but gave no date. During his time at Kew there were frequent importations of living plants from North America. John Lindley commented in 1840 that this was one of the finest of the American Cypripediums and was not uncommon in gardens in England. 'It, however, seldom lives above a year or two after its arrival. Those who manage it best treat it as a greenhouse plant, keeping it constantly under glass, in a moderately warm atmosphere, and very near the light until its leaves have withered, when it is removed to a dry shelf until its growing season returns.'

This seems strange advice for the cultivation of a plant whose native habitat is the margin of wet sphagnum bogs. A frequent companion plant, in the wild, is the attractive fern *Osmunda regalis* which also prefers damp habitats. The queen orchid can now be raised from seed without much difficulty and the importing of wild-collected plants has ceased.

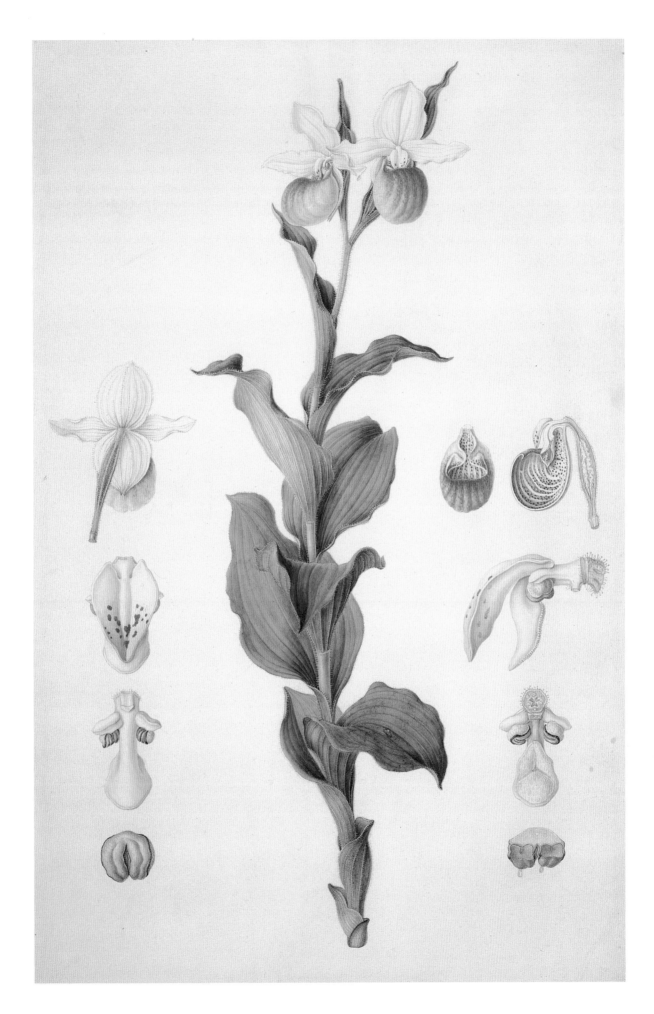

## *Dendrobium linguiforme* Swartz

COMMON NAME   tongue orchid
DISTRIBUTION   eastern Australia

Some orchids are easily recognized even when they are not in flower because they have distinctive leaves. In this species each leaf is shaped like a tongue (hence the specific epithet from the Latin *lingua* – 'tongue' and *forma* – 'shape') and also has a minutely rasping surface rather like that of an animal's tongue. The stem is short and usually prostrate on the bark of a host tree or, more commonly, on sandstone rock formations. The leaves are so tough that they can withstand exposure to full sun, even on dark coloured rocks. They may shrivel during a prolonged dry season but have the capacity to grow plump again as soon as the rains return.

The slender flowers are creamy or sparkling white with very narrow sepals and petals and a short curved lip. In Bauer's enlarged figure of a single flower one of the sepals has been removed to reveal the lip which is sometimes dotted with purplish blue. In the wild there are usually six to twenty flowers on each raceme. Many racemes may appear at a single flowering so there is a spectacular display.

This species is easily established and maintained in cultivation provided the plants are grown in plenty of light with good humidity and air movement.

The generic name *Dendrobium*, from the Greek *dendron* – 'tree', and *bios* – 'life', refers to the epiphytic habit of the first species described from this huge genus, *D. moniliforme* from Japan.

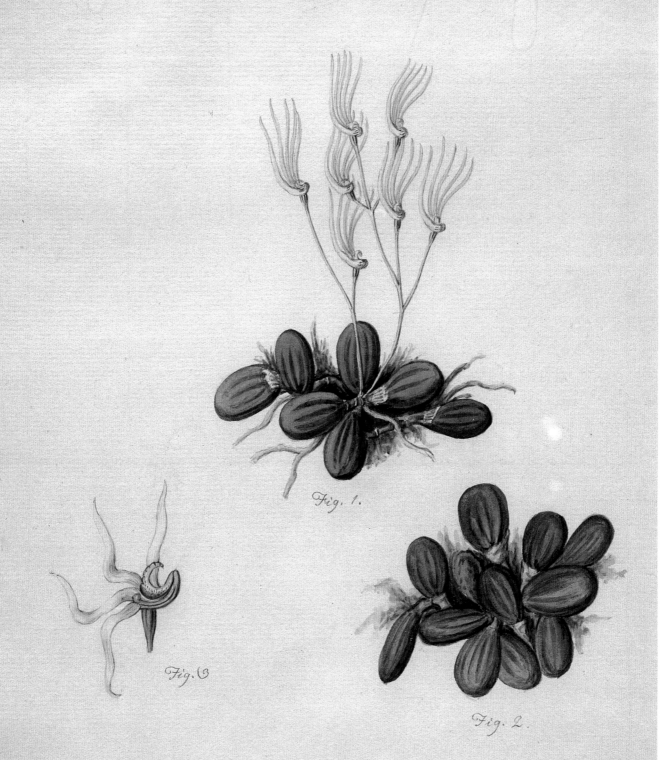

Fig. 1.

Fig. 3

Fig. 2.

# Dendrobium speciosum J. E. Smith

COMMON NAMES  rock orchid, king orchid
DISTRIBUTION  Australia: Queensland, New South Wales
and Victoria

The specific epithet *speciosum* means showy and it
is suitably applied to this spectacular lithophyte
from eastern Australia. Although this species is
found on trees in other parts of its range, the
typical variety which Bauer illustrated came from
near Port Jackson, now known as Sydney, New
South Wales, where it is almost always found on
outcrops of sandstone rock.

The waxy flowers are white, cream or yellow and
are produced in long racemes above the leaves at
the apex of each conical pseudobulb. They are visited by numerous insects including small bees. Large
globular fruits are produced if pollination is successful, each one containing many thousands of seeds.

This is one of the easiest Australian orchids in
cultivation, requiring cool and dry conditions
throughout the winter and bright light with plenty
of warmth and high humidity during the summer.
A coarse potting-mix that permits good drainage is
essential. Plants can also be established in slatted
baskets or on bark. In tropical and subtropical
gardens this species survives very well on a rock
garden unless the plants are grazed by orchid
beetles (*Stethopachys formosa*) which can be very
damaging. Plants in large containers produce a
marvellous floral display for spring flower shows.

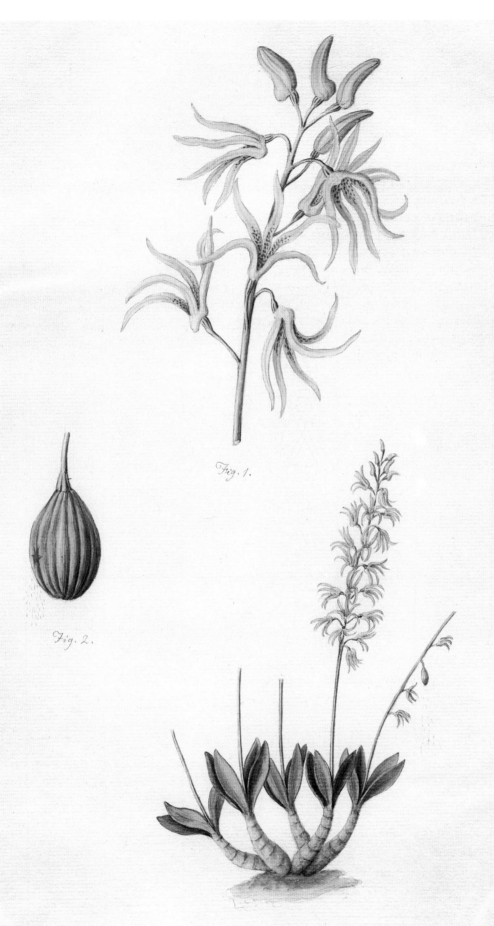

*Fig. 1.*

*Fig. 2.*

*Fig. 3.*

# *Dipodium punctatum* (J. E. Smith) R. Brown

COMMON NAME  pink hyacinth orchid
DISTRIBUTION   Australia: New South Wales, Victoria,
South Australia and Tasmania

This leafless, terrestrial orchid is usually described as a saprophyte, and is thought to be dependent on a mycorrhizal fungus for its nutrition. It grows in a wide variety of soils, but is usually found in close association with *Eucalyptus* trees. There is the possibility that it shares a complex association with both a tree and a fungus as has been shown recently with the subterranean orchid, *Rhizanthella gardneri*. All attempts to grow plants in cultivation have failed, though the transplanted rhizomes often produce one or two inflorescences before they die away.

Robert Brown founded his new genus *Dipodium* in 1810 on this species which had been described earlier by J. E. Smith from plants collected near Port Jackson. The name *Dipodium*, from Greek *di* – 'two, double', *podium* – 'small foot', refers to the two little stalks of the pollinia.

Flowering stems are an attractive sight in the forest and scrub of eastern Australia. They are up to a metre tall when fully developed and carry up to sixty flowers on each thick, reddish stem. Several flowering stems often appear together as Bauer painted them.

Fig. 1.

## Diuris aurea J. E. Smith (*left*)

COMMON NAME  golden donkey orchid

DISTRIBUTION  Australia: New South Wales

## Diuris sulphurea R. Brown (*right*)

COMMON NAMES  tiger orchid, hornet orchid

DISTRIBUTION  Australia: Queensland southwards to Tasmania

The golden donkey orchid flowers in the spring months and makes wonderful golden spots of colour among the grasses and sedges where it appears, both in open forests and in damp depressions. It is easily recognized among the other yellow-flowered species of the genus by its clear orange colour. Plants were introduced to Kew by George Caley in 1810, but this drawing was made from specimens sent back by Colonel William Paterson, Governor of New South Wales from 1800–10.

This is the type of the genus proposed by J. E. Smith in 1798. The name refers to the two lateral sepals which protrude below the flower rather in the manner of two tails (from the Greek, *dis* – 'two' and *oura* – 'a tail'). It is curious that the popular name refers to the two petals which are held above the flower rather in the manner of donkey's ears in some of the species, instead of the sepals.

This slender species is very widespread and often locally abundant. It bears only one or two grass-like leaves. The bright yellow flowers have large brown markings at the base of the dorsal sepal and on the lip.

Like most of the forty or so species of *Diuris*, it grows well in cultivation but can be difficult to flower unless the tubers are restricted within a small pot. In the wild, small colonies of plants produce one of the prettiest sights when they flower above the fallen brown leaves or sere grasses of winter at the time when fresh spring growth is just beginning.

*Fig. 1.*

*Fig. 2.*

## *Encyclia cochleata* (Linnaeus) Lémée

COMMON NAME   cockleshell orchid
DISTRIBUTION   Mexico south to Colombia and Venezuela;
Florida and the West Indies

This species was one of the first epiphytic orchids to flower in the collections at the Royal Gardens at Kew, only one year later than *E. fragrans* (Swartz) Lémée in 1787. The specific epithet *cochleata* refers to the lip which is shaped like a shell. This name was first suggested by the French missionary, explorer and botanist, Charles Plumier in 1703. Linnaeus placed it in the genus *Epidendrum* in the second edition of his *Species Plantarum* in 1763.

Although the genus *Encyclia* was proposed by W. J. Hooker in 1828, it was treated for many years as a section of *Epidendrum*. Dressler's studies of the genus in Mexico and his convincing arguments have resulted in its proper recognition since 1961. Lémée made the transfer of this species in 1955 in his *Flore de la Guyane Française*.

This widespread species grows in a wide variety of forest types, both in shady situations and in full sun. In sunny positions the leaves are often rather yellowish green and may become burnt at the tips. From Bauer's painting it rather looks as if the plant he saw may have been grown too near the glass when it was first cultivated at Kew.

# *Epipactis helleborine* (Linnaeus) Crantz

COMMON NAME   broad leaved helleborine
DISTRIBUTION   North America, Europe and northern Asia
as far eastwards as Lake Baikal and also in the Himalaya
in Pakistan

The broad leaved helleborine is one of the tallest of the European orchids though not the tallest member of the genus. *Epipactis gigantea* Douglas ex Hooker grows up to a metre tall in North America, while *E. africana* Rendle in Kenya and the highlands of Ethiopia is two or three times this size.

The broad leaves along the flowering stem and their distinctive venation make this orchid easily recognizable. The flowers are rather variable in colour, often rather dingy, but sometimes in bright shades of pink and green or suffused with violet. *Epipactis* is an ancient Greek name, for which the Greek *helleborine* was an alternative.

In Britain this species is most commonly found in woods or along their margins and in open spaces that receive shade for at least part of the day. It is very late in coming through the soil surface each year. The new shoots appear in June and flowers are borne from the end of July until September. The flowers seem to be attractive to wasps who are busy at this time of the year.

"August 2ⁿᵈ 1811."

# Epipactis helleborine (Linnaeus) Crantz

COMMON NAME  broad leaved helleborine
DISTRIBUTION   North America, Europe and Asia as far
eastwards as Lake Baikal and the Himalayas in Pakistan

This common orchid was well known long before it was described by Linnaeus as a species of *Serapias*. It was mentioned in Turner's *The seconde parte of William Turner's Herball* in 1562 and in many subsequent works. Infusions and other concoctions from the rhizomes and roots were recommended for the treatment of gout and other maladies.

Its discovery in the state of New York in 1879 was a great surprise in a relatively well-botanized area. How it arrived there is a mystery, but it is always regarded as a European plant which has somehow achieved an introduction, spread, slowly at first and then more aggressively, until now it is almost a weed in some areas. It has also been collected and introduced into gardens. From some of these it has escaped and it is now widespread across the cooler parts of the continent of America.

These drawings were made in August 1800 but the study on the previous page was not completed until 1811.

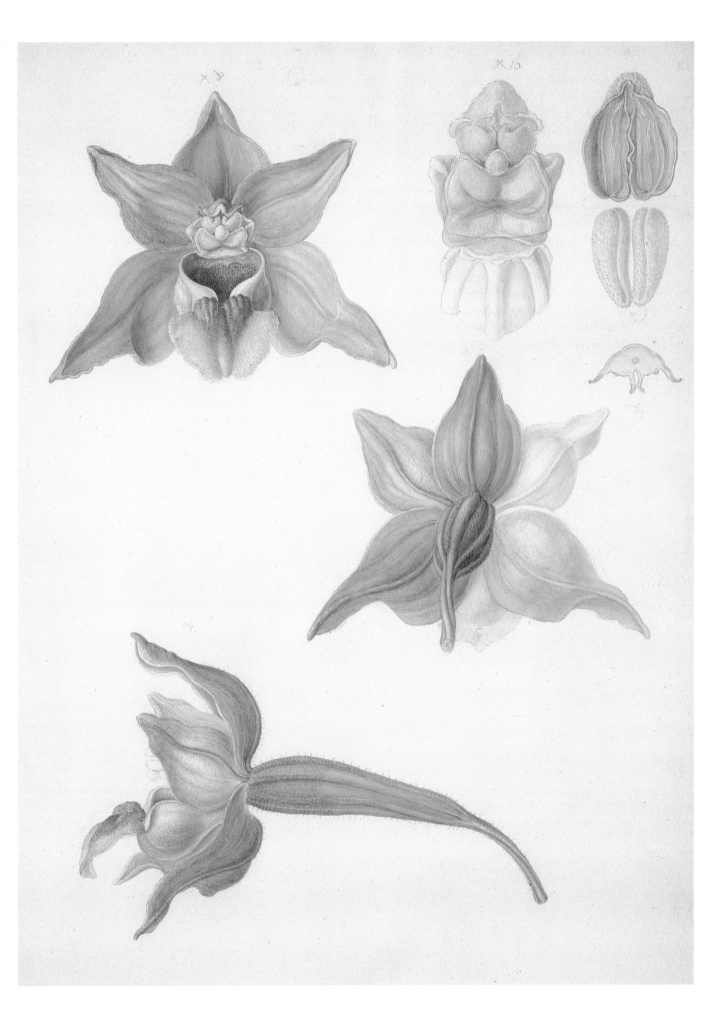

# *Epipactis palustris* (Linnaeus) Crantz

COMMON NAME  marsh helleborine
DISTRIBUTION  Europe and temperate Asia

This is a species of the wetlands, marshes and duneslacks. It has become very much reduced in numbers in recent years because of the degradation of so many habitats by drainage and pollution. In the Royal Botanic Gardens, Kew a few plants grow well and flower every year in a woodland situation. There is some hope that the wild plants will not only succeed in their few remaining habitats but will also spread into others that are undisturbed nearby.

The large white lip makes this one of the finest of the twenty-odd species of *Epipactis*. The hairy ovary has a slender pedicel so that the flowers move in the slightest breeze. A marsh full of moving inflorescences, early in July, is a striking sight. Many different insects visit and pollinate the flowers. Bees, flies, beetles and even spiders have been found inside the flowers. They appear to contact the pollinia when they withdraw from the flower, having been pushed into the right position as they stumble over the callus at the central constriction of the lip.

"August 2. 1799"

Epipactis palustris W

# Galearis spectabilis (Linnaeus) Rafinesque

COMMON NAMES  showy orchis, purple hooded orchis
DISTRIBUTION  eastern United States and southeastern Canada

This species was one of the few North American orchids named by Linnaeus, as *Orchis spectabilis*, in his *Species Plantarum* in 1753. The epithet *spectabilis* 'remarkable or notable', refers to its showy flowers which are superficially similar to those of other members of the European genus *Orchis*. The large leafy bract below each flower and the pair of large leaves between which the inflorescence arises give the plants a somewhat distinctive appearance. The plants arise from a short fleshy rhizome, instead of tubers as in *Orchis*. In 1833 the American botanist Rafinesque proposed the new genus *Galearis* to accommodate this rather different North American species. From the Latin word *galea* – 'a helmet', the name refers to the way the sepals and petals are held in the form of a hood or helmet arching over the column.

This is one of the commoner orchids of the woodlands in eastern North America and it is also one of the earliest of all wild flowers. It can be found in undisturbed woodlands of various kinds before the leafy canopy has unfurled in the spring. It is so early that flowers may be spoiled by late frost or snow. It is usually found as single growth plants, though many may grow together in an extensive colony, but sometimes small clumps of plants are found with a number of growths flowering together. Colour is rather variable, and both pure white and pure pinkish purple flowers are recorded. The most attractive are those with the pretty contrast between the pale pink hood and the creamy white lip.

Plants of this species were introduced to Kew by Sir Joseph Banks's collector Francis Masson in 1801.

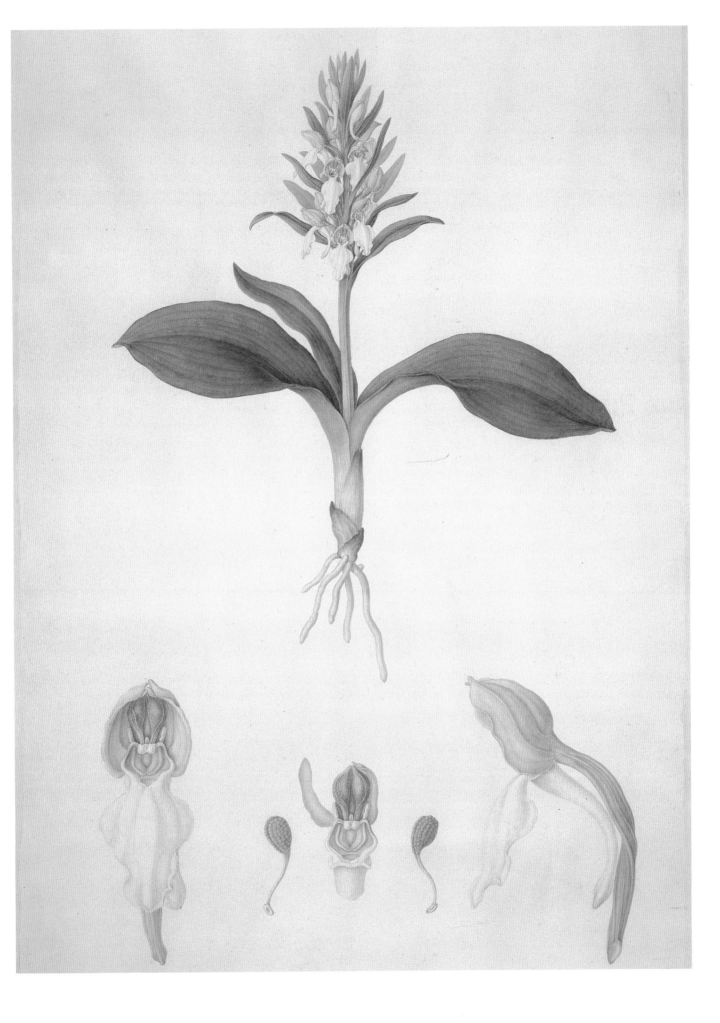

## Glossodia major R. Brown (left)

COMMON NAMES wax lip orchid, parson-in-the-pulpit
DISTRIBUTION Australia: southeast Queensland, southwards to Tasmania

Robert Brown described two species of *Glossodia* (from the Greek *glossodes* – 'tongue-like', referring to the tongue-shaped callus at the base of the lip) when he established the genus in 1810. This species is slightly larger than the other, *G. minor*, and has a very distinctive lip. It is narrowly heart-shaped, bright purplish blue towards the apex, with a white cushion on either side below and a solid yellow callus at the base. Although Bauer must have made his drawing from pressed specimens, the features of the lip are remarkably life-like and the hairy leaf and stem are well depicted. Bauer also made a sketch of the outer surface of the flower (figure 2) to show the short glandular hairs on the sepals.

This is a widespread and common orchid in eastern Australia which is the only part of the world where blue orchids are found in any number. It is very exciting to come across small colonies of plants flowering profusely early in the spring. They are a great surprise to someone familiar with the orchids of the tropics and the northern hemisphere.

## Caladenia caerulea R. Brown (right)

COMMON NAME blue Caladenia
DISTRIBUTION Australia: widespread from southeast Queensland to Tasmania and in Western Australia

Robert Brown named this genus *Caladenia* (from Greek *kalos* – 'beautiful', *aden* – 'gland') in 1810 in allusion to the glands or calli which ornament the lip. In the species illustrated in figure 3, they are bright yellow and adorn the margins of the midlobe which is rather small. The bright blue colour of this species is rather unusual in this genus of more than a hundred species, not all of them properly named and described as yet. Many are delicate or fragile in appearance and have been named the fairy orchids in some areas. Others have greatly elongated sepals and petals and are called spider orchids.

All the species are terrestrial and they often favour stony ground. They grow among grasses and small shrubs in lightly shaded woodlands and scrub. A colony of many plants in flower in the early spring is a most attractive sight.

Fig. 2.

Fig. 1.

Fig. 3.

# Goodyera repens (Linnaeus) R. Brown

COMMON NAME creeping lady's tresses
DISTRIBUTION throughout the cooler parts of the north temperate zone, in Asia, Japan, America and Europe

Two species of *Goodyera* were in cultivation at Kew when Robert Brown established the genus in 1813. He named it in honour of an English botanist and scholar, John Goodyer (1592–1664), who lived in Hampshire, was highly esteemed for his critical knowledge of British plants and translated Dioscorides' Greek text into English. The first species Brown listed was the smaller, *G. repens*, so named because its horizontal stems appear to creep across the woodland floor except when they put up a terminal, upright inflorescence. The second, *G. pubescens*, is larger with a more dense inflorescence of many flowers. Both bear their leaves in rosettes produced annually. They are bluish green and in North American specimens at least they are often attractively veined with silver.

About forty species of *Goodyera* are now recognized, mostly occurring in damp and humid habitats. The creeping lady's tresses has the flowers arranged in a loose spiral, and thus shares a vernacular name with some species of the related genus *Spiranthes* which also have this kind of inflorescence. Its growing habit is quite different however. It is found in mossy pine- and birch-woods and the creeping, fleshy stems produce rather few roots.

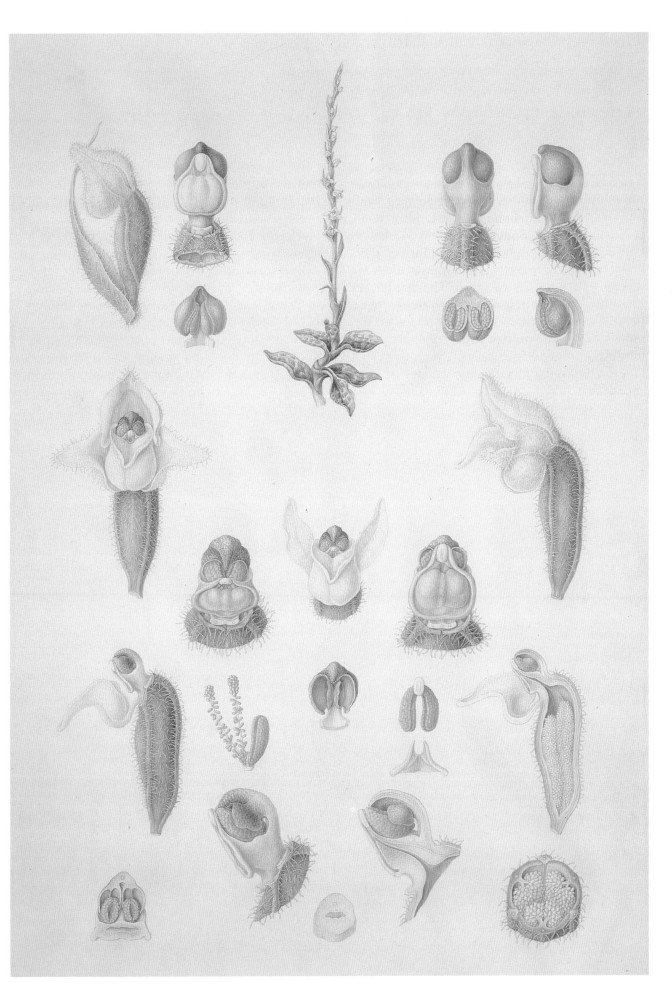

# *Himantoglossum hircinum* (Linnaeus) Sprengel

COMMON NAMES  lizard orchid, tadpole orchid
DISTRIBUTION  western Europe, extending as far east as parts
of Austria and Czechoslovakia

This tall orchid is usually found on sunny grass-land slopes, sometimes at the edges of woodland and also in rather new grass covering sand dunes. It is most common in France where it is often a conspicuous plant at the roadside in June or July. Until recently there were rather few locations for it in England, but in the last few years it has become established in a number of sites near roadsides and on golf courses. These situations have given rise to speculation that the tiny seeds may be spread on clothing or in mud on vehicles.

Underground there are large, oval tubers which put up their first leaves in the autumn. The leaves survive through the winter but may become damaged at the tips in severe weather. By the time the strong flowering stem appears from the centre of the rosette, the lower leaves have usually withered. The shaggy, rather greyish coloured inflorescence is striking even from a little distance.

Bauer's painting of the whole plant is preserved at Göttingen. It appears to be a copy of a painting by Franz Scheidel published in Nicolaus von Jacquin's *Flora Austriacae*, t. 367 (1776). Bauer made the drawings of the enlarged flowers reproduced on the next page much later, and they are preserved among his collection of paintings of British Orchids in the Natural History Museum at South Kensington, London.

*Orchis hircina* W.ᵒ 15.

# Himantoglossum hircinum (Linnaeus) Sprengel

COMMON NAMES  lizard orchid, tadpole orchid
DISTRIBUTION  western Europe, extending as far east
as parts of Austria and Czechoslovakia

The individual flowers of the lizard orchid need close inspection to understand the structure of the lip with its curiously elongated and slightly twisted midlobe. The name of the genus, from the Greek words *himas* – 'belt, thong or rein' and *glŏssa* – 'tongue', refers to this feature. Bauer's enlarged drawings also reveal the intricate and delicate colouring and detail of the flowers, especially on the inner surface of the petals and at the base of the lip.

This orchid has acquired many popular names in different parts of Europe but is most widely known as the lizard orchid. Its distinctive 'ranke or stinking smel or savour like the smell of a goat', to quote Gerard, prompted early authors to name it *Tragorchis, Testiculus hirci, Orchis odori hirci*, from the Greek, *tragos* and Latin *hircus*, both meaning 'he-goat'; hence the Linnaean epithet *hircinum*. This curious and somewhat rancid smell of the mature flowers is attractive to a variety of insects, including small flies, bees and sometimes bluebottles. The exact composition of the 'fragrance' of the lizard orchid was revealed in 1991, by the Swiss chemist, Roman Kaiser. As with many other orchids it contains a whole spectrum of chemical compounds which are also found in other flowers.

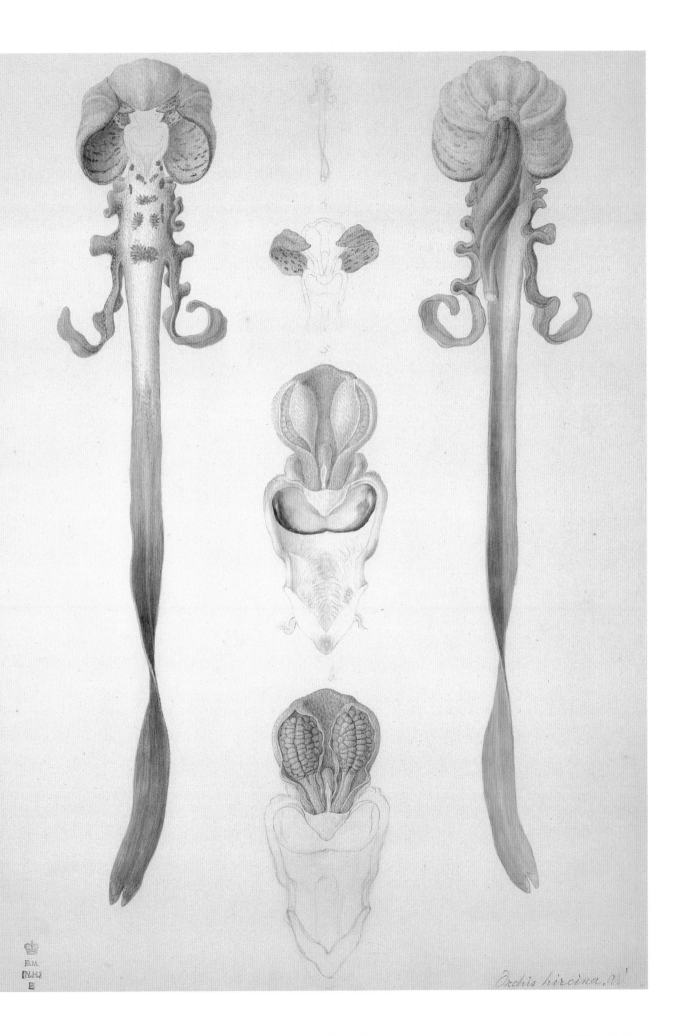

*Orchis hircina. N.*

## *Isochilus linearis* (Jacquin) R. Brown

DISTRIBUTION  widespread in tropical America

The small flowers of this leafy orchid are always borne at the ends of the stems. The parts of the flower are more or less equal in length and the name of the genus was proposed by Robert Brown in 1813 because of this feature: from the Greek words *isos* – 'equal' and *cheilos* – 'lip'.

Nicolaus von Jacquin described this species first in 1763, as *Epidendrum lineare* in his illustrated work, *Selectarum Stirpium Americanarum Historia*. It was based on material collected by Jacquin himself in Martinique, his main base during his stay in the West Indies from 1755 to 1759.

Bauer depicted this orchid at least twice. The illustration preserved at Göttingen is a simple, colour washed drawing and appears to be a copy of the Jacquin illustration. The painting reproduced here was found among Bauer's 'Kew Plants' at South Kensington and is annotated 'West Indies'. It is not dated, but may have been prepared from a plant seen by Brown when he was preparing the account of the orchids at Kew for the second edition of Aiton's *Hortus Kewensis*. It had been introduced to Kew by Edward Elcock in 1791. This species is the type of the small genus *Isochilus*.

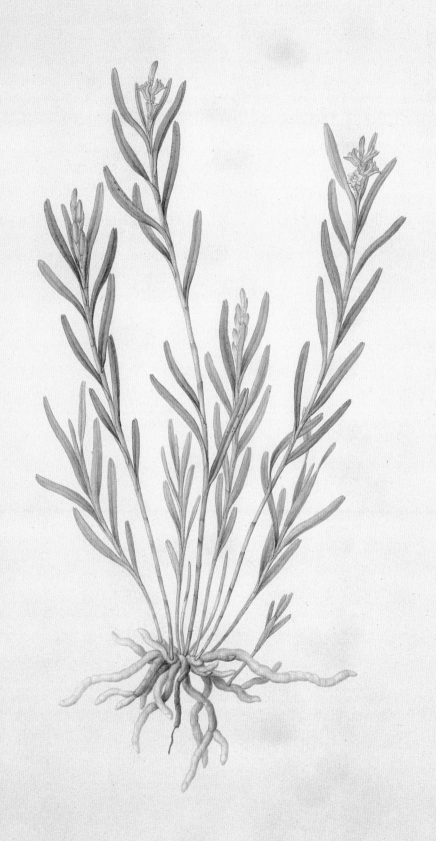

# *Limodorum abortivum* (Linnaeus) Swartz

COMMON NAME  violet limodore
DISTRIBUTION  Europe, mainly in the countries
around the Mediterranean, and Israel

The violet colouring of the tall plants of this orchid makes it easy to identify. It lacks leaves and is often described as a saprophyte. However, there have been suggestions that it is parasitic, at least for part of its life history, and it is nearly always found in habitats where pine trees are also growing. One could speculate that there may be a complex relationship with the tree roots through a mycorrhizal fungus as has been reported for the Australian orchid genus *Rhizanthella* and a species of *Melaleuca*.

This strange yet spectacular orchid is widespread throughout the warmer parts of Europe and up to 1,750 m altitude. It is usually found among bushes and grassland in the shade of pines, or in mixed woodland where pines of various species form part of the canopy. It flowers in the summer months and, provided there has been sufficient rain in the preceding winter months, the stems may reach a height of 80 cm or more.

*Limodoron* is a Greek word for one of the broomrapes, parasitic plants in the family *Orobanchaceae* which at first sight this orchid somewhat resembles.

# *Liparis lilifolia* (Linnaeus) L. C. Richard ex Lindley

COMMON NAMES   lily-leaved twayblade, large twayblade, mauve sleekwort, purple scutcheon
DISTRIBUTION   eastern North America, including southern Ontario

The generic name *Liparis* is derived from the Greek word *liparos* – 'fat, greasy or shining', referring to the soft and rather fleshy leaves of many of the species. The flowers are also rather distinctive, with their very narrow petals and small attractive lip. Most of the two hundred or more species have green or dark red flowers and are attractive for the well-flowered inflorescence as a whole rather than for their individual beauty.

Two species of *Liparis* are widespread in eastern North America, and the other, *L. loeselii*, also occurs in Europe where it is becoming a rare plant. The larger species is often called a twayblade because of its two broad leaves which are still enlarging while it is coming into flower. They arise directly from a small pseudobulb produced during the preceding year. Sometimes plants are found with short chains of pseudobulbs, each one representing a previous year's growth.

In the wild *L. lilifolia* is found in well-drained but damp habitats, on the banks of woodland streams and in wooded areas where the shade is not too dense. It is easily introduced to cultivation at the dormant stage of growth, before the leaves arise. One of the first orchids introduced to English gardens from North America, it was cultivated by Peter Collinson in 1758. Bauer recorded that the plant he illustrated on 23 June 1811 had come from North America.

# *Listera ovata* (Linnaeus) R. Brown

COMMON NAMES  twayblade, adder's tongue, sweethearts

DISTRIBUTION  Europe and widespread in Asia to Siberia and north India; also in Canada where it appears to have been introduced

If an orchid can be described as a weed, then this plant probably qualifies as one. It is extremely widespread, sets seed prolifically, and seems to have no difficulty surviving in damaged habitats or appearing in new ones. Large plants with long racemes of green flowers are common along many country roadsides throughout Europe. Despite the effects of modern intensive agriculture, it is often found at the edge of arable fields, in pastures, gardens and public open spaces.

The genus was named by Robert Brown in honour of Martin Lister (1638–1711), an English naturalist, physician to Queen Anne, and friend of the famous botanist, John Ray. The herbalist John Gerard used twayblade in ointment and balsam for healing wounds.

Most of the twenty or more species of this genus, which is spread around the north temperate zone, are much smaller than *L. ovata*. It has a handsome pair of ovate leaves which are borne halfway up the stem arising from an underground rhizome. There may be a hundred or more green flowers appearing over a long season. They are pollinated by a variety of small insects, including flies and beetles, and each ovary develops into a globular fruit. The flowering stem and outer surface of the flowers is glandular and sticky to touch. This may be an added attraction to insect visitors.

*Listera ovata. R. Br.*

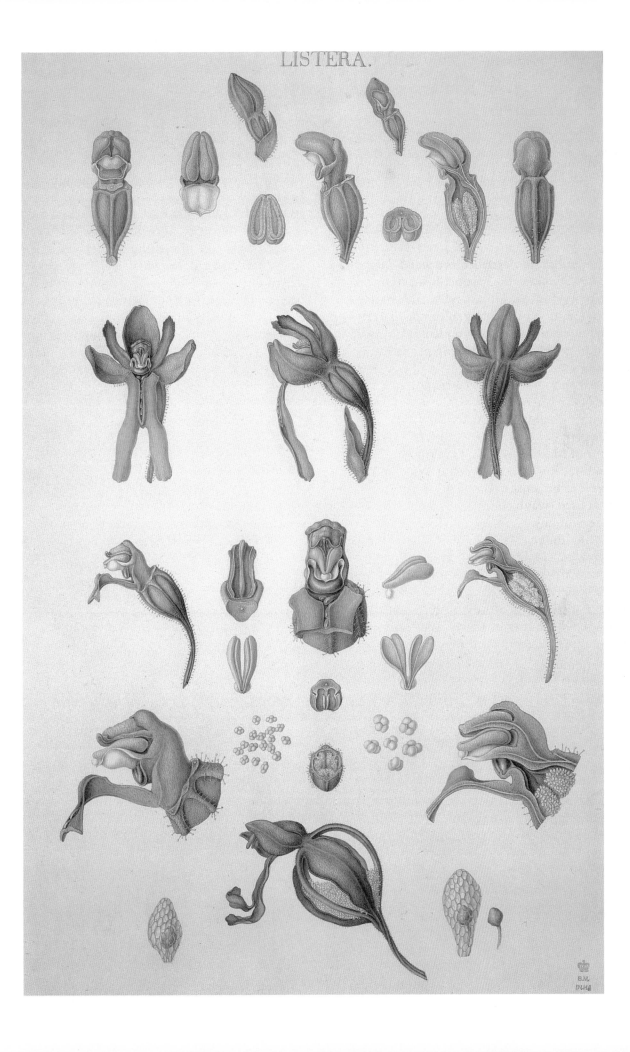

# *Maxillaria coccinea* (Jacquin) L. O. Williams ex Hodge

DISTRIBUTION   West Indies, both Greater Antilles and Lesser Antilles

This widespread epiphytic orchid was first collected by the French botanical explorer Charles Plumier before 1703. The Dutch-born Austrian botanist Nicolaus von Jacquin also collected it, in Martinique, and named it *Epidendrum coccineum* in 1760. He illustrated it in his *Selectarum Stirpium Americanarum Historia*, t. 205. Bauer's illustration, which is now in the Library of the University of Göttingen, is clearly a copy of this plate.

This species was introduced to Kew by Alexander Anderson in 1790. Robert Brown recorded it as *Ornithidium coccineum* Salisbury in the second edition of Aiton's *Hortus Kewensis* in 1813. It was finally transferred to *Maxillaria* in 1954.

The bright rose or carmine flowers are borne singly on slender stems which arise in clusters in the axil of the light green leaves. It seems not to have been widely cultivated in Europe but is in fact easy to grow in a well-drained pot or basket and tolerates cool temperatures at night for part of the year.

## *Maxillaria subulata* Lindley

DISTRIBUTION  Brazil

This plant was received at the Royal Gardens at Kew early in the nineteenth century and illustrated when it flowered there in November 1818. A small specimen which resembles part of the plant illustrated is preserved in Lindley's orchid herbarium at Kew. Lindley did not describe the species until 1832 but he was able to prepare a detailed description from Bauer's illustration. It is interesting to note that the flowers on the leafy plant are pencilled in and then drawn and coloured in separate drawings nearby at a greater magnification so that their structure is shown very accurately.

The genus *Maxillaria* is one of the larger epiphytic genera of the American continent with over 300 species. The name was proposed by the Spanish botanists Ruiz and Pavon with reference to the fancied resemblance, when seen from certain angles, of the column and lip to the open jaws of an animal (from the Latin word *maxilla* – 'jaw').

The dark-coloured species like *M. subulata* have an unpleasant scent and are probably pollinated by flies. They are members of a small group of about seven Brazilian orchids which have a pair of awl-shaped leaves on each flattened pseudobulb.

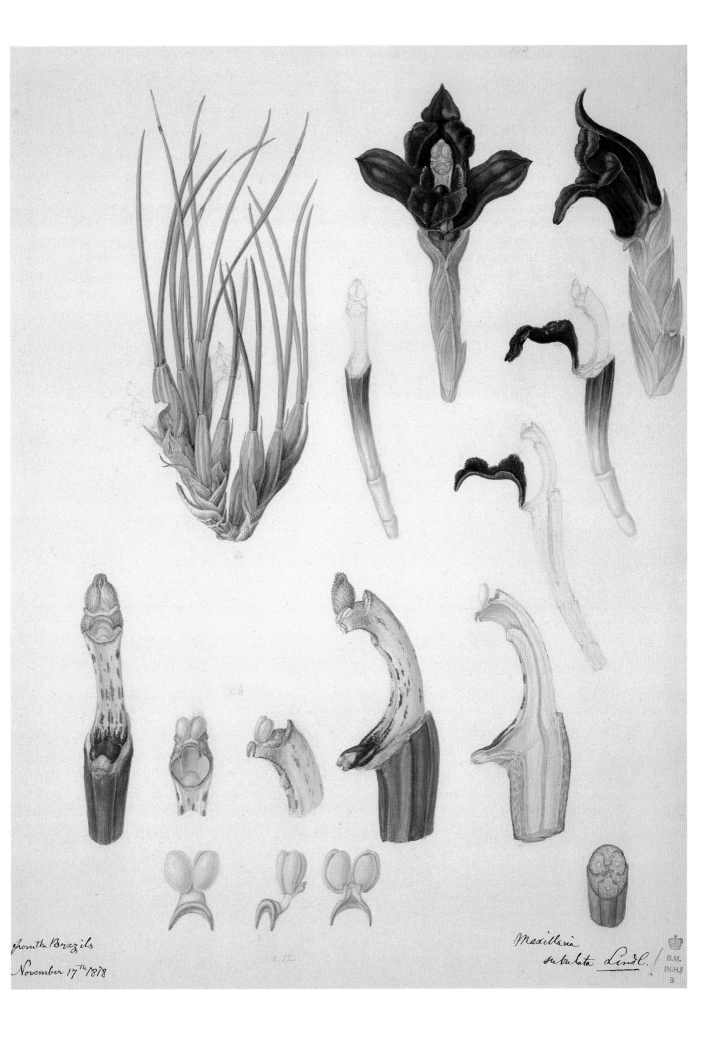

from the Brazils
November 17th 1818

Maxillaria
subulata Lindl.

## Oncidium ampliatum Lindley (above)

COMMON NAME   yellow bee (in Trinidad)

DISTRIBUTION   Central America from Costa Rica southwards, Panama, Trinidad, Venezuela, Colombia and Peru

The almost square flowers of this species of the large genus *Oncidium* are distinctive in the clear yellow of the large, bilobed lip, which is paler on the back, and in their large petals. The callus on the base of the lip is also an important feature in species recognition. It was this callus which provided Swartz with the character for the generic name (from the Greek word *onkos* – 'a tumour or swelling').

John Lindley published his description of this species in 1833. It had been discovered by the explorer Hugh Cuming in Costa Rica about 1830 and introduced by Richard Harrison of Liverpool who flowered it in 1835. Bauer's drawings were made from a plant introduced to Kew Gardens from Trinidad in March 1834.

## Oncidium sphegiferum Lindley (centre and below)

DISTRIBUTION   Brazil

When John Lindley described this species in the *Botanical Register* in 1843, he noted that it was a new introduction from Brazil, flowering in Messrs Loddiges nursery. However, Bauer's drawings are clearly dated May 1834 and refer to a plant growing in the garden of the Horticultural Society at Chiswick.

This species comes from a restricted area around Rio de Janeiro where it occurs with three other species which have a papillose, cushion-like crest on the lip, *O. divaricatum*, *O. pulvinatum* and *O. harrisonianum*. The oblong shape of this crest and the bright orange colour of the sepals and petals make *O. sphegiferum* clearly recognizable, though it may have been confused with two of the other species in the group when it was first introduced.

The epithet *sphegiferum* means 'wasp-bearing', from the Greek *sphex* – 'wasp'.

Oncidium! from Trinidad
K. G. March 14th 1834.

X 3

X 10

X 20

X 3

X 400

X 20

X 6

X 6

X 400

Oncidium?
Hort. S. Garden May 25th 1834.

# *Oncidium baueri* Lindley

DISTRIBUTION   West Indies, Central and South America:
Mexico to Brazil and Peru, Virgin Islands and Martinique

It is appropriate that John Lindley named an orchid with complex flowers in honour of Francis Bauer when they collaborated in producing the series of *Illustrations of Orchidaceous Plants* (1830–38). The drawings of this colourful species had been made in 1804 from herbarium specimens which were somewhat faded. However the detail and markings are absolutely correct. The wings on either side of the column are shown particularly clearly.

This species is widely distributed in the hotter parts of the American continent and adjacent islands. It has often been introduced to cultivation but its long straggling inflorescence, often more than 3 m long with many branches, makes it somewhat awkward to manage in a glasshouse. It produces many flowers which are somewhat smaller as well as slightly different in structure from those of *O. altissimum* (Jacquin) Swartz with which it has sometimes been confused. Lindley called it the 'Lofty *Oncidium*' in the *Botanical Register* in 1833 (t. 1651) and in that year a plant with stems more than 2 m long received a medal from the Horticultural Society of London (now the Royal Horticultural Society).

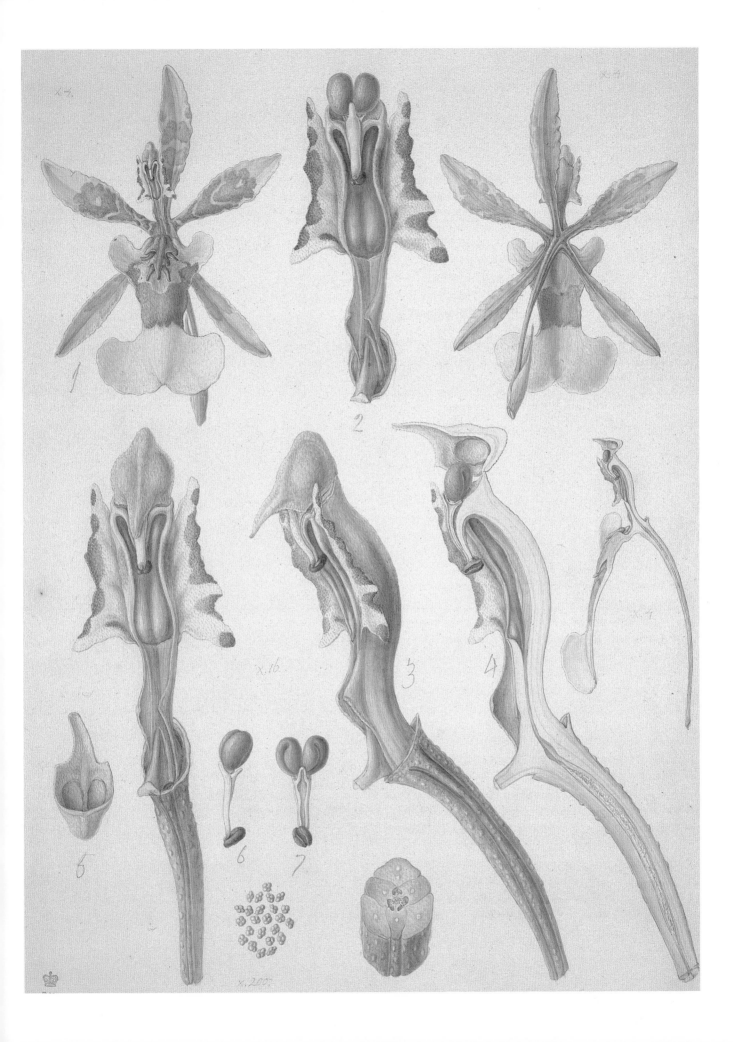

# *Ophrys apifera* Hudson

**COMMON NAME** bee orchid

**DISTRIBUTION** Europe, throughout the Mediterranean area from Israel and Turkey westwards to North Africa and north to the British Isles

The genus *Ophrys* is restricted to Europe, North Africa and the Middle East in its distribution. The genus as treated by Linnaeus in his *Species Plantarum* (1753) contained sixteen species, of which all but one have now been transferred to the genera *Aceras, Chamorchis, Corallorhiza, Hammarbya, Herminium, Liparis, Listera, Malaxis, Neottia* and *Spiranthes*. The name is derived from the Greek word *ophrys*, which means 'eyebrow'. There has been much conjecture about the reason for the use of this name: needing names for genera, Linnaeus adopted names of classical origin without much regard for their original application. Pliny applied *Ophrys* to a two-leaved plant, identity unknown, which was used to blacken eyebrows or hair.

Somewhere between thirty and sixty species of *Ophrys* are recognized today. The variance in numbers is related to taxonomic opinion which is very varied. Some botanists recognize few species and many subspecies and varieties while others prefer to recognize every distinct taxon at the specific level.

The bee orchid is one of the most widespread species. It is also the only one which seems to rely on self-pollination as a means of reproduction, at least in the northernmost parts of its distribution. The stalks of the pollinia are longer and more slender than in other species of *Ophrys*. Soon after the flower opens they shrink so that the pollinia are pulled out of their pouches and fall forwards in front of the stigma. They are held securely in this position by the viscidia which stay in place. Soon a drop of rain or puff of wind is sufficient to bring them in contact with the sticky stigma to which they then become attached. In the Mediterranean area the bee orchid is pollinated by solitary male bees of the genus *Eucera* which fly around looking for female bees and are deceived by the scent of the orchid's bee-like flowers into alighting upon them, as mentioned on the next page.

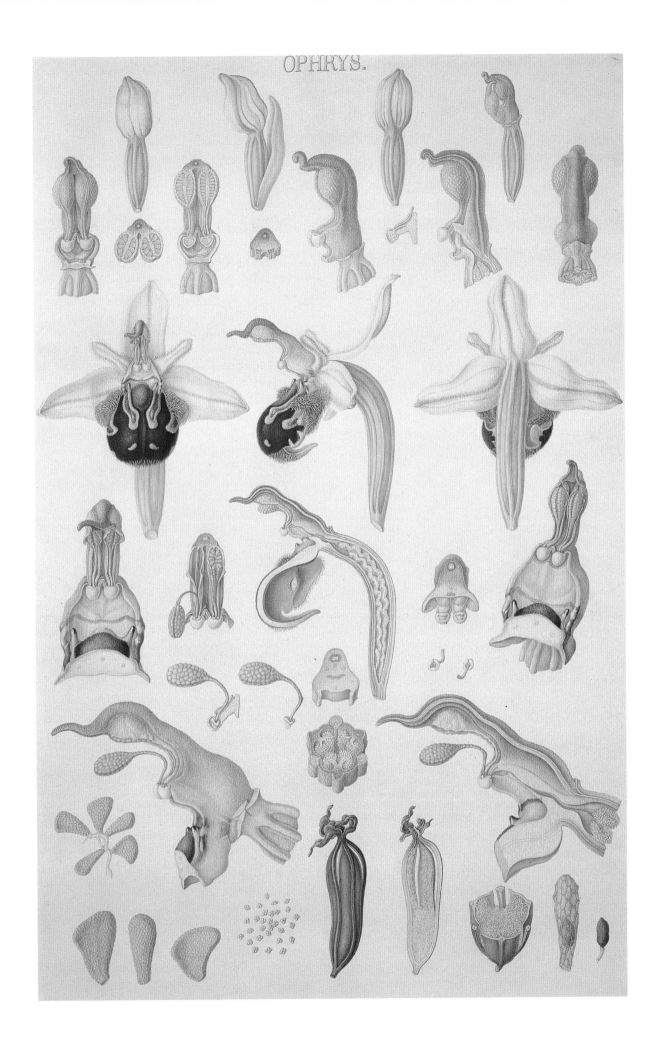

## *Ophrys apifera* Hudson

COMMON NAME  bee orchid

DISTRIBUTION  Europe, throughout the Mediterranean area from Israel and Turkey westwards to North Africa and north to the British Isles

Bauer was fascinated by the bee orchid and made many illustrations of it, including a variety of drawings showing enlargements of the whole flower and of its parts. There are many such detailed drawings on the previous page.

The greatly enlarged flowers show the remarkable shape and texture of the lip which give to this species both its common name and specific epithet, from the Latin words *apis* – 'a bee' and *-fera* – 'bearing or carrying'. It looks like a small pink flower on which a bee has just landed. In fact it is the scent of the flower which is more attractive to a solitary male bee than its supposed resemblance to the female of the species. Various phytochemical studies have confirmed the hypothesis that the flower 'scent' mimics the female sex pheromone and that this is the primary attractant to the male insect. Having landed on the flower, the copulation instinct is further aroused by the superficial structure and shape of the lip.

Although the flowers of the thirty or more *Ophrys* species produce no nectar or pollen, they are each attractive to a particular species of insect. The relationship between orchid and insect ensures the preservation of the species, but accidents occur and cross pollination by humans is not unknown. Thus a large number of interspecific hybrids have now been documented.

# *Ophrys holoserica* (Burmann filius) W. Greuter

COMMON NAME   late spider orchid

DISTRIBUTION   Europe, Mediterranean region from Israel
westwards to eastern Spain and northwards to southern Austria
and Germany and to a few localities in southeast England

Widely known under the synonym *O. fuciflora*
(F. W. Schmidt) Moench, the late spider orchid is
larger and perhaps more spectacular than the bee
orchid. In many parts of Europe they grow
together on calcareous soils. They are easily
distinguished by the shape of the lip which in the
late spider orchid has a forward pointing, rather
fleshy lobe like a horn at its apex. The markings
on the lip vary from plant to plant, and the overall
coloration of the flower is also extremely variable.
The sepals may be white, greenish pink, or almost
red and the small triangular petals are usually similar. Hybrids between the two species are recorded
and have been named *O.* × *albertiana* Camus.

# *Ophrys holoserica* (Burmann filius) W. Greuter

COMMON NAME  late spider orchid
DISTRIBUTION  Europe, Mediterranean region from Israel
westwards to eastern Spain and northwards to southern Austria
and Germany and to a few localities in southeast England

The first discovery of an *Ophrys* species, particularly one of those with pink sepals and a large hairy lip, is an experience that is never forgotten. It is so exciting that one can go year after year to look for plants. Many of the species fluctuate in numbers. There may be thousands one year, following a good setting of seeds a few years earlier, and only a few the next. Recent population studies have shown that mature plants die after flowering well for one or a few seasons. Many seeds are produced at a single flowering, as Bauer's drawing of a cross section of the ovary makes clear, but there are relatively few years in which the weather and other environmental factors are entirely suitable for their germination.

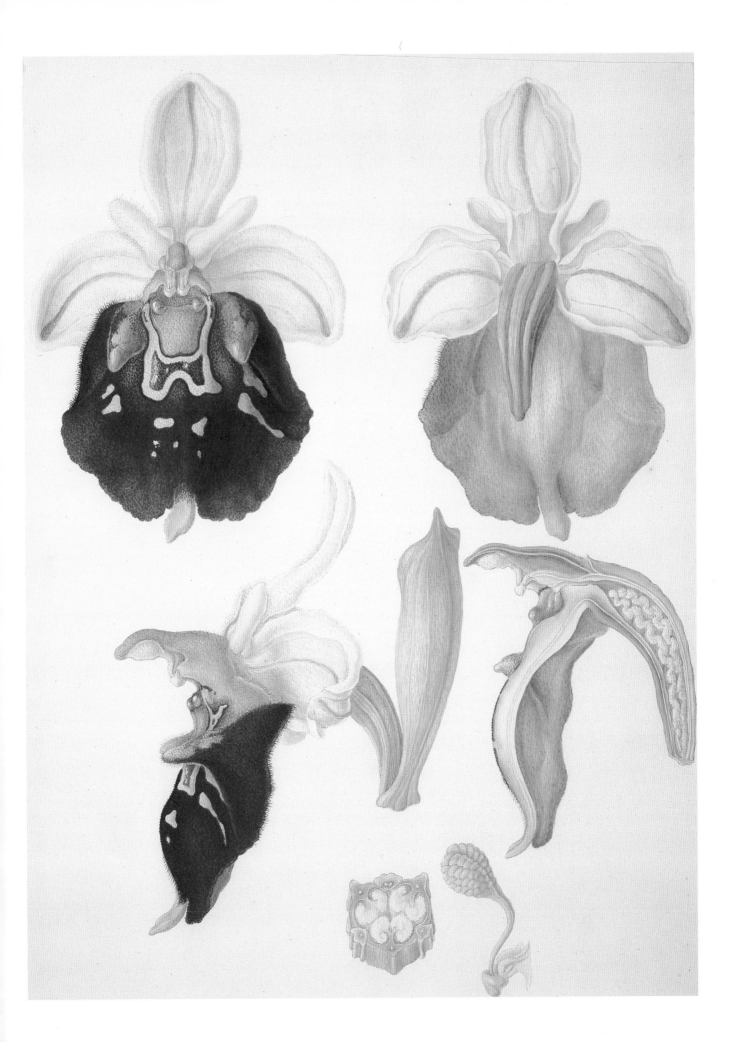

## *Ophrys insectifera* Linnaeus

COMMON NAME  fly orchid

DISTRIBUTION   Europe, from Norway and central Sweden
south to France and eastwards to Hungary and Russia

This species is the most northerly of the genus *Ophrys* in its distribution and is rarely seen around the Mediterranean. It is the most difficult to find in the shady woods where it usually occurs, but once a single plant is located, others are usually discovered in the vicinity. Though often regarded as rare, it may be that this species is frequently overlooked because of its rather inconspicuous colouring. Individually the flowers have been likened to a row of flies with softly hairy bodies perched on a spike of green flowers. Their scent attracts two wasp species belonging to the genera *Gorytes* and *Argogorytes*. After landing on the lip facing towards the column, they perform pseudocopulatory movements in the course of which the pollinia become attached to the head and are carried away to the next flower.

## *Orchis morio* Linnaeus

COMMON NAMES   green-winged orchid, green-veined orchid, clown spikes (in Scandinavia)
DISTRIBUTION   Europe, widespread and extending into the Near East and North Africa

This small orchid is one of the earliest species to flower in most parts of Europe. The basal rosette appears the previous autumn and the leaves are pressed to the soil throughout the winter. Early in spring the central spike appears, always rather short, and bearing 8–12 flowers. They vary in colour through pale and darker pink to a rich magenta and white forms also occur.

The green-veined sepals cohere to the dorsal sepal and petals to make a helmet-shaped structure at the top of the flower. It has been suggested that this resembles a clown's hat and gave rise to the Swedish name *Göknyckel* or *Göknycklar*, (from *gök* – 'cuckoo, fellow', *nyckel* – 'key'). However, it is unlikely that Linnaeus had this local name in mind when he adopted the old name *Orchis morio* in his

*Species Plantarum* (1753): *morio* is the Latin word for 'a fool'. *Orchis morio* is the name used by Caspar Bauhin in 1623 who cited *Testiculus morionis* and *Cynosorchis morio* as 16th-century synonyms. Linnaeus did not mention *Göknyckel* as a vernacular name.

This species was once a very common orchid in parts of the British Isles, Germany and Scandinavia. Mixed with cowslips on calcareous soils, in damp meadows on clay soils and even in woodlands on acid soils it made an exciting sight early in spring. Because of intensive farming and urbanization it is now much more restricted in its distribution than formerly, though large populations can still be found in undisturbed situations.

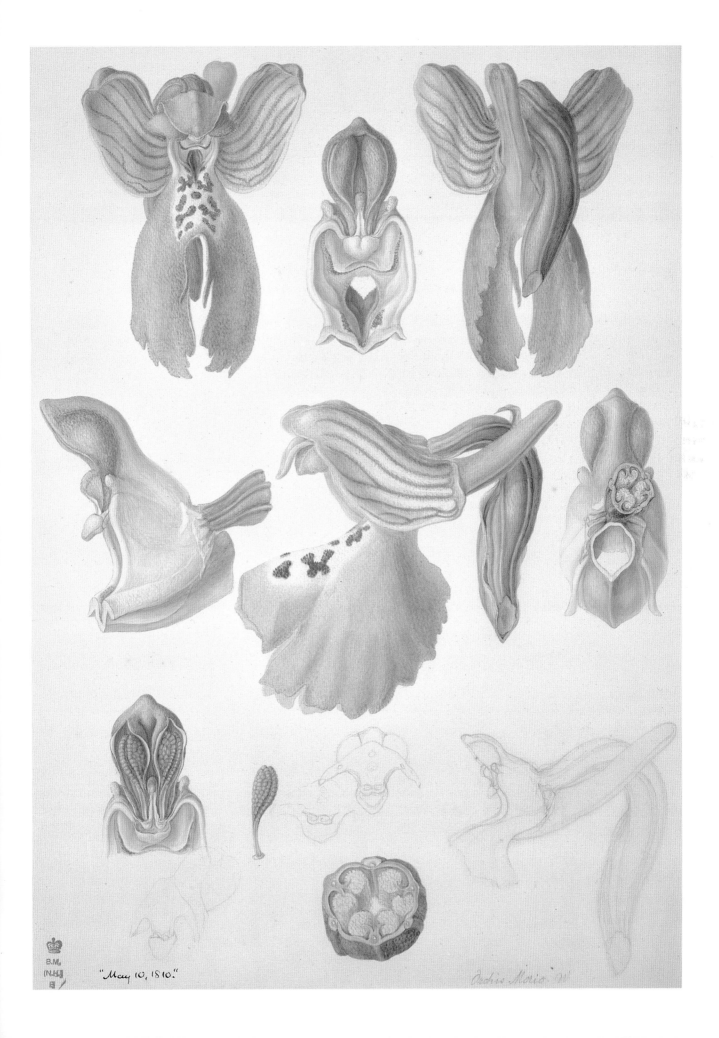

"May 10, 1810."

Orchis Morio

## *Orchis purpurea* Hudson

COMMON NAME  lady orchid
DISTRIBUTION  Europe, throughout the Mediterranean area
from Turkey westwards to France and North Africa, with a few
localities in England

This is one of the tallest orchids in Europe with many-flowered inflorescences rising 50–80 cm above a basal cluster of leaves. They arise each spring from a pair of ovoid tubers to which the ancient Greek and Latin writers referred when they used the name *Orchis* ('testicle'). Linnaeus followed this earlier usage and that of the Greek herbalist Dioscorides who used this name for several different plants with paired underground tubers. In 1836 John Lindley made the name *Orchis* the basis of the family name *Orchidaceae* for the whole of the orchid family.

The lady orchid is a woodland plant and is also found along the margins of woods, in open clearings, scrub and occasionally in grassland. It grows best on calcareous soils but is often severely damaged by rabbits. Its distribution is similar to that of the military orchid, *Orchis militaris* Linnaeus, and hybrids between the two species have been reported.

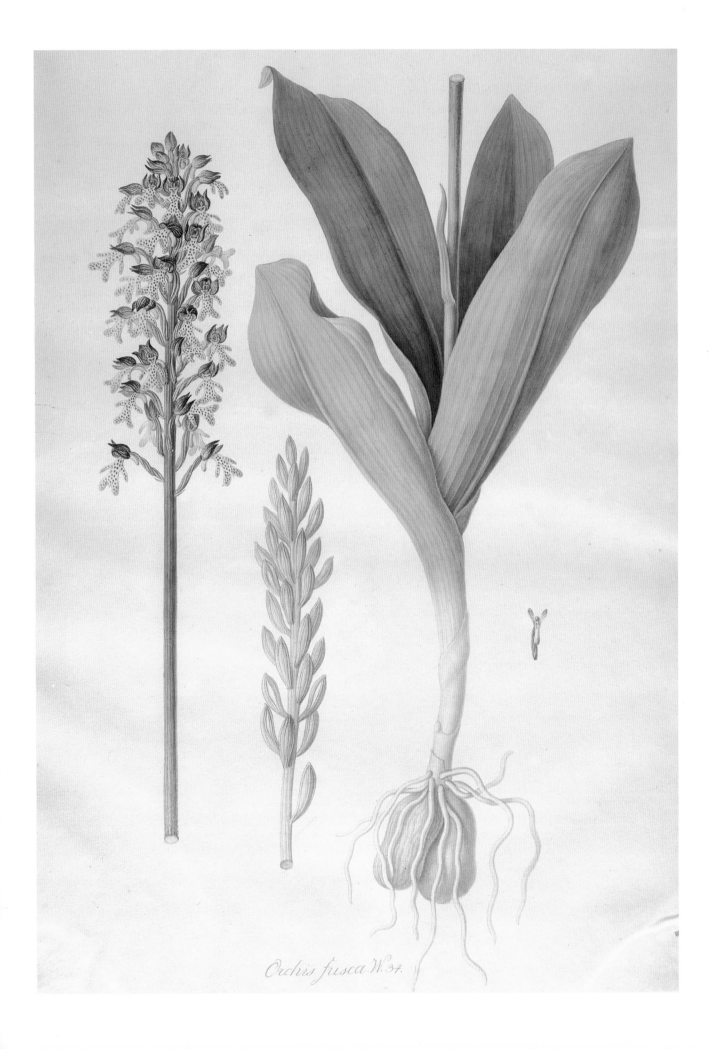

*Orchis fusca* W. 34.

## Orchis purpurea Hudson

COMMON NAME  lady orchid
DISTRIBUTION  Europe, throughout the Mediterranean area
from Turkey westwards to France and North Africa, with a few
localities in England

The enlarged views of lady orchid flowers reveal both their structure and the origin of the common name. The top of the flower is composed of the dark or purplish sepals and petals. It is thought to resemble the head or bonnet of the lady. The enormous lip thus becomes her full cotton skirt with an arm on either side. The dark spots are seen to be clusters of hairs, arranged in rows or scattered over the surface. There is a short spur at the base of the lip. No other large orchid has this combination of colouring and such a wide lip.

The lady orchid hybridizes with other species of *Orchis* where they grow together in many parts of Europe. Intergeneric hybrids are also known, particularly with the man orchid, *Aceras anthropophorum*. These have been named × *Orchiaceras macra* (Lindley) Camus.

# *Orchis ustulata* Linnaeus

COMMON NAME  burnt orchid
DISTRIBUTION  Europe, from southern Sweden eastwards to
Russia and the Caucasus, west to eastern Spain, France and
England, absent from the true Mediterranean

On his visit to the island of Oeland in 1741, Linnaeus noted this orchid, 'krutbrännare', which he said was 'an incomparably appropriate name, since the flowers in the spike are burning red, but the little buds in the top are black, like the picture of a fire'. This obviously caused him to name it *Orchis ustulata* in the *Species Plantarum* (1753) from the Latin *ustulo* – 'burn, scorch'.

This is one of the smallest species of *Orchis* and it is not easy to see in the short grasslands where it occurs. It is usually found in rather dry habitats.

Although many of its former habitats have been ploughed up, it is one of those species whose distribution is maintained by man's activities. Undergrazing, or grazing at the wrong time of year, can lead to its extinction locally.

Small size was no deterrent to Bauer who enjoyed making a full and complete record of this species in June 1811, even including its minute seeds. In colouring it is somewhat like a miniature lady orchid but the lip is much narrower and with fewer spots.

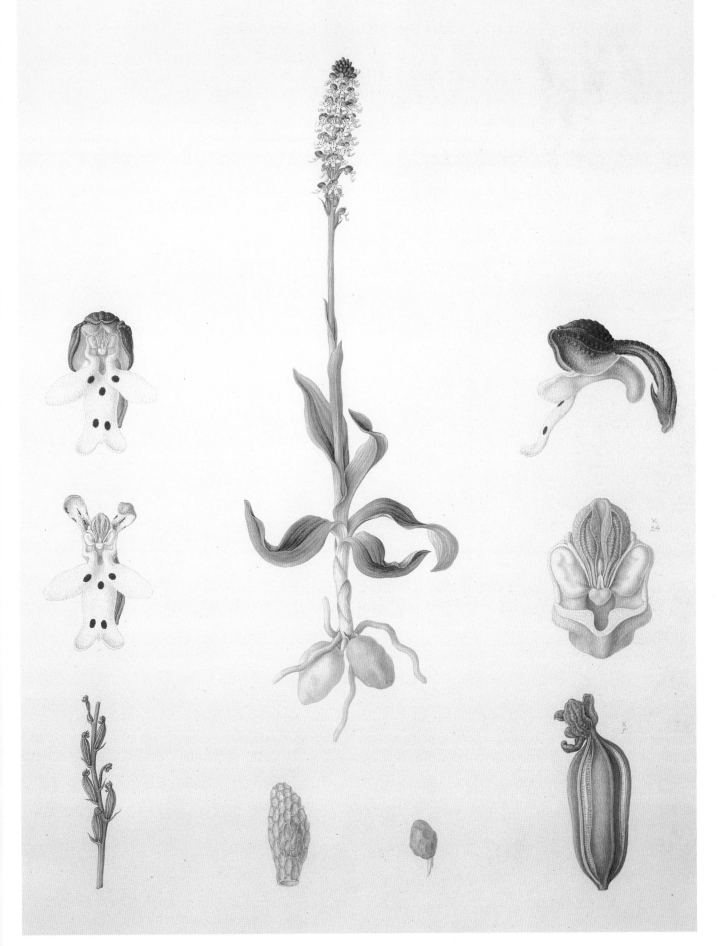

# *Paphiopedilum venustum* (Wallich) Pfitzer ex Stein

DISTRIBUTION Northeast India (Meghalaya), eastern Nepal, Sikkim and Bhutan

The introduction of the Asiatic slipper orchids to cultivation began early in the nineteenth century and at that time they were all included with the genus *Cypripedium*. In 1886 Pfitzer separated them generically under the name *Paphiopedilum* (literally, the slipper of Aphrodite, whose major temple was at Paphos on Cyprus) and many transfers to this genus were formally made by Stein in his *Orchideenbuch* (1892).

This species was the first to be grown in England and the first of the Asiatic species to be described. It was discovered by Dr Nathaniel Wallich in Sylhet in 1816. He suggested the name for it and the species was illustrated for the first time in 1820 in *Curtis's Botanical Magazine* (t. 2129). The specific epithet *venustum* – 'charming, beautiful, elegant, like Venus' refers to its appearance.

The leaves are also a distinctive feature of this species, and were described by W. J. Hooker as 'spotted like a *Gasteria*'. This is the only Indian species of *Paphiopedilum* with tessellated markings on the upper surface of the leaves and the purple coloration of the lower surface is also unusual. Both these characters are present, however, in other species of the genus which are found further east.

Bauer's dissections illustrate the remarkable structure of the column in this genus. It has a shield-shaped staminode overlying the three-lobed stigma. Only three other genera of orchids, *Cypripedium*, *Phragmipedium* and *Selenipedium* are similar, with a pair of stamens one on each side of the smooth stigma. The sticky pollen grains which the stamens yield to a passing insect are also portrayed.

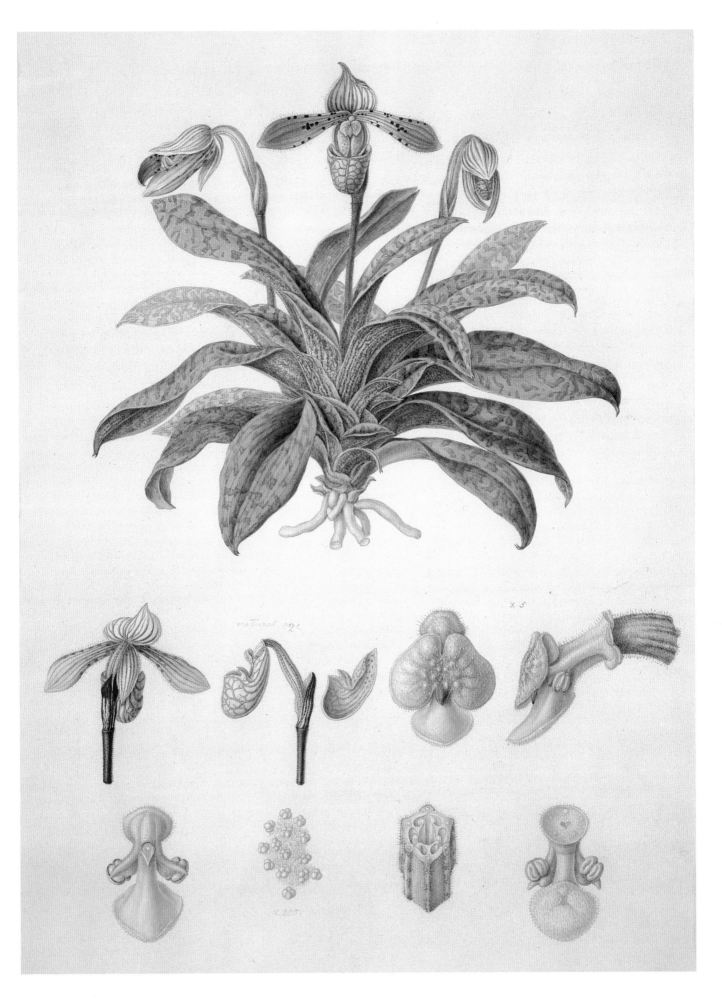

natural size

× 5

## Phaius flavus (Blume) Lindley

DISTRIBUTION   widespread in southeast Asia, from the Himalayas (Nepal to Bhutan), to Assam, Thailand, China, Malaysia and Java

This handsome terrestrial orchid was sent to Kew about the year 1822 by Dr Nathaniel Wallich, Superintendent of the Calcutta Botanic Garden from 1815 to 1841, who spent a year in Nepal in 1820. He suggested the name *P. maculatus* which Lindley published in 1831, and which referred to the bright yellow spots that are nearly always present on the leaves. However, Lindley also published the combination *Phaius flavus* for a Javan plant which had been described earlier by the German botanist Carl Ludwig Blume (1796–1862). Once it became apparent that there was very little difference between these two species over their wide distribution in Asia, the name *P. flavus* was accepted as the earlier and therefore correct one.

*Phaius* is derived from the Greek word *phaios* – 'swarthy', an allusion to the yellow-brown shades of many of the flowers in the genus. It was proposed by the Portuguese botanist João Loureiro in his *Flora Cochinchinensis*. His type was *P. grandifolius*, also pre-dated by an earlier name, *P. tancarvilleae*, which was the first tropical orchid to flower at Kew. It was wonderfully illustrated by James Sowerby in William Aiton's *Hortus Kewensis* (1789).

Some thirty species of *Phaius* are now recognized and distinguished from the related genus *Calanthe* by the large, free column and by its very short or absent spur at the base of the lip. All the species are terrestrial plants, often growing in swampy ground. Their large plicate leaves make an interesting feature among a collection of epiphytic orchids, but their size is sometimes difficult to manage in a temperate glasshouse.

# *Platanthera bifolia* (Linnaeus) L. C. Richard

COMMON NAME   lesser butterfly orchid
DISTRIBUTION   throughout Europe and Asia

The generic name *Platanthera* refers to the wide anther in the flower of all the species of this genus, from the Greek adjective *platys* – 'wide or broad' and the modern botanical term *anthera* – 'anther' which in classical Latin meant 'a medicine compounded of flowers'. This character distinguishes it from the large tropical genus, *Habenaria*, in which many of the hundred or so species now recognized were placed originally. *Platanthera bifolia* is the species on which the French botanist Louis Claude Richard based his description of the genus in 1817.

There are two rather similar species of *Platanthera* in Europe, the greater and lesser butterfly orchids. Both have a tall spike of greenish white flowers which are sweetly scented at dusk and pollinated by moths which fly in the evening. Both species usually have a pair of broad leaves at or just above the base of the flowering stem. They often grow together in mixed populations though *P. chlorantha* tends to prefer calcareous soils while *P. bifolia* grows on many soil types. The difference between them lies in whether the two sacs in the anther lie close to each other and are more or less parallel (*P. bifolia*) or at a broadly diverging angle above a very wide stigma (*P. chlorantha*). Hybrids have been reported between the two species and many different forms of flowers are found on plants from different habitats.

## *Platanthera lacera* (Michaux) G. Don

COMMON NAMES  ragged fringed orchid, green fringed orchid
DISTRIBUTION  northeastern USA and southeastern Canada

The fringed orchids of North America are a striking sight in many damp habitats in the summer months. The tall spikes of flowers in various shades of pink, purple, white, green and bright orange-yellow stand out clearly among the surrounding vegetation. This species is one of the least conspicuous and, perhaps because it is less easily seen among the prevailing greenness of its wild habitats, it is still a very common orchid.

The specific epithet refers to the distinctively fringed margin of the lip which often appears torn or ragged in nature (from the Latin word *lacera* – 'torn'). Bauer has drawn the lobes and fringes with great precision and regularity. The most luxuriant specimens with the finest fringes are found in New England.

In the wild this species usually grows in swamps and marshes, bogs, meadows, in damp woodland glades, swampy woods and occasionally in wet fields. It is rarely cultivated today but in the early days of orchid growing it was listed as a *Habenaria* by the nurserymen Conrad Loddiges and sons and grown by them until about 1832. Like many other species in the genus, the fringed orchid is pollinated by several different moths.

## *Pterostylis rufa* R. Brown

COMMON NAME   rusty hood
DISTRIBUTION   Australia: widespread in the east
from southeast Queensland to Tasmania

The deep rusty red flowers of this small orchid are long-lasting and in cultivation the plants may bloom for six months producing up to fifteen flowers successively. Usually there are fewer on a slender stem arising from a basal rosette of leaves which often wither by the time the flowers appear. In the wild it is one of the most drought-tolerant of Australian orchids, often found in dry situations. But its large tubers, overlapping leaves, and sites near rocky ground where run-off increases the available moisture, all help it to survive in apparently inimical surroundings.

The rusty hoods are sometimes grouped together in the genus *Pterostylis*, partly following the famous botanist George Bentham. He found them so difficult to study, as pressed specimens, that he lumped them all together as *P. rufa* in his account of the orchids in *Flora Australiensis* (1873). Australian botanists now recognize about forty different species.

They are all pollinated by small gnats which land on the hinged lip. Their weight triggers the slender stalk at its base so that they are flung forward into the hood. From here they can find a way out by the aid of the light that penetrates the translucent windows in the back of the hood. In crawling up and out they pass the column and remove the pollinia. Bauer's detailed drawings and dissections illustrate the details of this fascinating flower as a whole and with its sepals and petals removed.

## *Satyrium erectum* Lindley

DISTRIBUTION  South Africa:
Namaqualand, southwest and
south Cape Province

The Greek name *Satyrion* originated in remote
antiquity for a plant which excited lust, as various
Mediterranean orchids were then reputed to do,
and so was associated with the lascivious Satyrs.
All the species of *Satyrium* are easily recognized by
the twin spurs at the base of the lip which is held
on the upper side of the flower. The lip is enlarged
and helmet-shaped so that there is a fanciful
resemblance to a devil with a pair of horns. The
Swedish botanist, Olof Swartz, used the name
*Satyrium* for a genus of about a hundred terrestrial
orchids with these characteristic flowers. They
mostly occur in Africa, but three are found in
Madagascar and two in Asia.

This pretty species grows in sandy soils in the
southwestern Cape and especially in the district
around Tulbagh. Bauer's drawing of a complete
plant and his superb series of illustrations of buds
and flowers illustrate the characteristics of the
genus very well. The development of the column
and anther are shown particularly well in the buds
and flowers from which the sepals, petals and lip
have been removed. The drawings were prepared
in 1800 from a plant grown in the Royal Gardens at
Kew. It had been received from the astronomer,
Sir John Herschel, who collected it in the Cape
Province of South Africa. He found it growing in
clay soils that are baked by the summer sun when
the plants are dormant.

Many species of *Satyrium* can be grown in
cultivation if the tubers are kept dry without
dehydrating for several months during the
dormant season. They are often lost, however,
through the ravages of rot brought on by watering
prematurely, or to predators such as mice or snails.

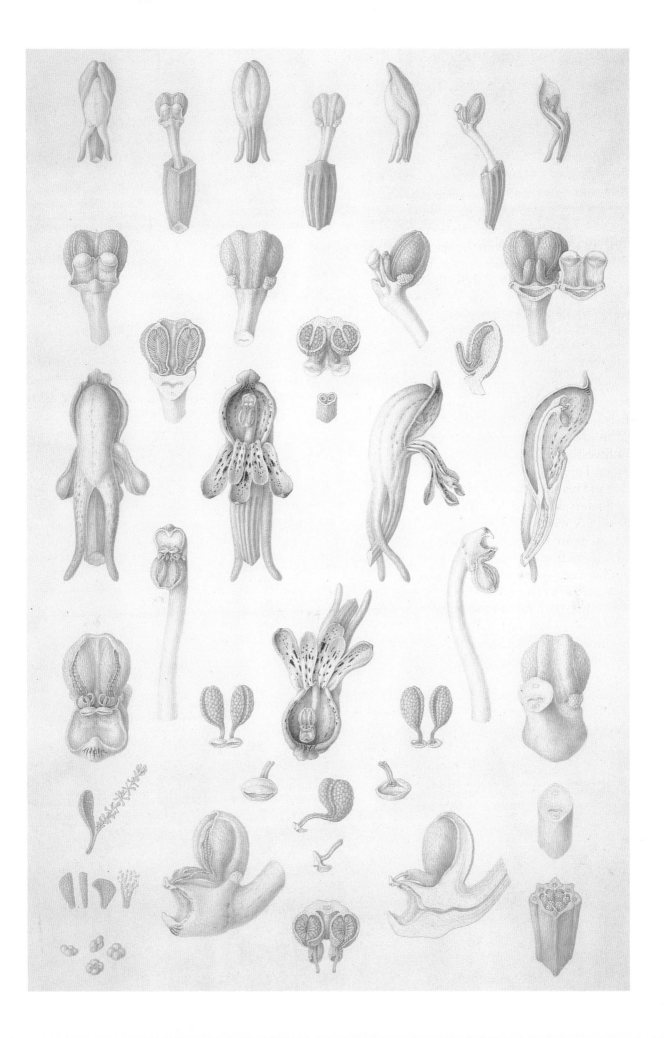

## *Stanhopea insignis* Frost ex Hooker

DISTRIBUTION   Ecuador, Peru and Brazil

The generic name *Stanhopea* was proposed by John Frost in honour of Philip Henry, Earl Stanhope (1781–1855) who in 1829 had just been elected President of the London Medico-Botanical Society from which Frost himself was expelled in 1830 for notorious behaviour. William Jackson Hooker formally published the name and description of the species illustrated here in *Curtis's Botanical Magazine* (t. 2948 and t. 2949; 1829). It was one of the first Stanhopeas introduced to cultivation and had flowered at Kew for the first time in 1827. The flowers are easily recognized by their almost complete covering of small spots and by the heart-shaped apical lobe of the lip. About thirty species are now known.

Their complex flowers are notorious for their quick development, fleshy substance, wonderful fragrance and short lifespan. Often they remain in perfect condition for only three days. They are also well known for appearing from their swollen inflorescences immediately below the pseudo-bulbs. In this way they expose themselves to visiting bees in the forests where they grow on the large branches of trees. In cultivation, however, the flowers remained hidden from growers who tried to establish the plants in clay pots. It was only when a pot was accidentally broken that the old flowers were discovered among the compost. After this the plants which had apparently never flowered in cultivation were grown in shallow slatted baskets and their flowers, which find their way out during the summer months, were much admired.

## Stenorrhynchos speciosum (Jacquin) L. C. Richard

DISTRIBUTION   Central America and the Caribbean region: Mexico south to northern South America and the West Indies

*Stenorrhynchos* is often included in *Spiranthes* but the plants lack the conspicuous spiral arrangement of flowers in that genus and their flower structure differs in several details. It was established by the French botanist Louis Claude Richard in 1818. The generic name comes from the Greek *stĕnos* – 'narrow' and *rhynchos* – 'snout, nose'; the epithet *speciosum* means showy. Nicolaus von Jacquin was the first to publish an illustration of this pretty orchid, labelled *Neottia speciosa*, in his *Icones Plantarum Rariorum* (t. 600) in 1793. Plants were introduced to Kew from the West Indies about 1790 by Sir Brooke Boothby.

In the wild *S. speciosum* grows both epiphytically in damp forests on tree trunks as well as on rocks and in the ground among bushes and grassland. It is easily cultivated and forms an attractive display in a well-drained compost. The rosette of dark green leaves is surmounted by a reddish inflorescence which is long lasting. The flowers are overtopped by the pink or red bracts and the inner surface of the lip is white.

Francis Bauer.                    Neottia speciosa.

# *Xylobium variegatum* (Ruiz and Pavon) Garay and Dunsterville

DISTRIBUTION   Costa Rica, Colombia, Venezuela and south to Bolivia and Brazil

Until rather recently this widespread species was known as *Xylobium squalens*. It was originally described as *Dendrobium squalens* by Lindley who studied a plant established in the Loddiges nursery which came from the vicinity of Rio de Janeiro. He transferred the name to *Xylobium* when he proposed the genus in 1825 but later became uncertain about this change and placed it tentatively in *Maxillaria*. His new generic name, which is now the accepted one for this taxon, referred to the epiphytic habit of the plants he knew and was derived from two Greek words, *xylon* – 'wood, timber' and *bios* – 'life'.

During the course of their monumental studies on the orchids of Venezuela, Garay and Dunsterville discovered an earlier name than Lindley's for this species. The Spanish botanists Ruiz and Pavon had described it as *Maxillaria variegata* when they collected material in Peru in 1798. Thus in 1961 the name *Xylobium variegatum* was finally published.

About thirty species of *Xylobium* are now known from the American tropics. Plants in this genus differ from those in *Maxillaria* in having plicate leaves and inflorescences bearing few to many flowers instead of a single one. The flowers are often rather drab, being cream or yellow suffused with red or purplish brown. They are partly hidden by the large leaves of which there are two on each compressed pseudobulb.

Further reading – *see* page 155

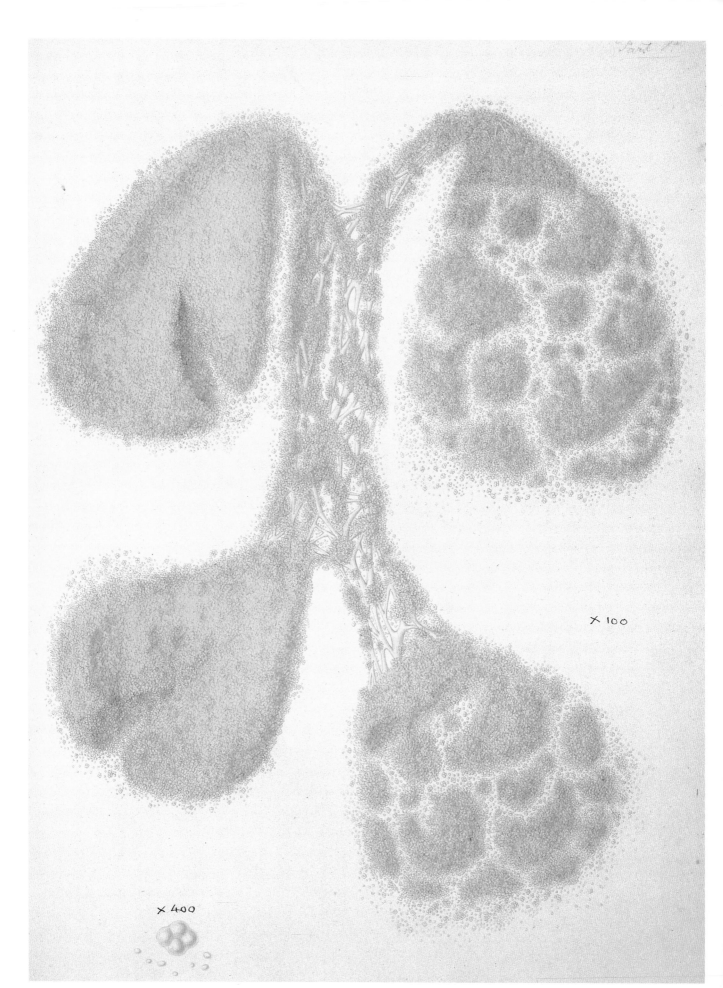

X 400

The greatly magnified pollinia of *Bletia purpurea*
(see page 22)

# Bibliography

for *Francis Bauer (1758–1840), Kew's First Botanical Artist*

AITON, W. 1789. *Hortus Kewensis*. 3 vols. London.

AITON, W. T. 1810–13. *Hortus Kewensis*. 2nd edn. 5 vols. London.

ANON. 1841. Francis Bauer. *Annals and Magazine of Natural History* 7: 77–78, 439–444.

BAUER, F. A. & LINDLEY, J. 1830–38. *Illustrations of Orchidaceous Plants*. 4 parts. London.

BLUNT, W. & STEARN, W. T. 1950. *The Art of botanical Illustration*. London.

FULFORD, R. 1933. *Royal Dukes, Queen Victoria's Father and 'Wicked Uncles'*. London.

GREENE, E. L. 1909. *Landmarks of botanical History*. Washington, D.C. [Reprinted 1983, Stanford, California].

KRONFELD, E. M. 1921. Jacquin des Jungeren botanische Studienreise 1788–1790, aus den unveröffentliche Briefe herausgegeben. *Beihefte zum Botanische Centralblatt* 38ii: 132–176.

LYSAGHT, A. M. 1971. *Joseph Banks in Newfoundland and Labrador, 1766*. London.

MEYNELL, G. 1983. Francis Bauer, Joseph Banks, Everard Home and others. *Archives of Natural History* 11: 203–221.

NISSEN, C. 1951. *Die botanische Buchillustration, ihre Geschichte und Bibliographie*. 2 vols. Stuttgart.

NOLTE, M. J. 1989. *Ferdinand Bauer. The Australian Natural History Drawings*. London.

OLBY, R. 1970. Bauer, Ferdinand Lucas. Bauer, Franz Andreas. In C. C. Gillespie (ed.), *Dictionary of Scientific Biography* 1: 520–521.

PRITZEL, G. A. 1871–77. *Thesaurus Literaturae botanicae*. 2nd edn. Leipzig.

REINIKKA, M. A. 1972. *A History of the Orchid*. Coral Gables, Florida.

SCHEER, F. 1840. *Kew and its Gardens*. London.

STEARN, W. T. 1960. Franz and Ferdinand Bauer, masters of botanic illustration. *Endeavour* 19: 27–35.

STEARN, W. T. 1967. Sibthorp, Smith, the 'Flora Graeca' and the 'Florae Graecae Prodromus'. *Taxon* 16: 168–178.

STEARN, W. T. 1989. William Hooker (1779–1832), illustrator of flowers and fruits, and his associates. In F. A. Roach & W. T. Stearn, *Hooker's finest Fruits*: 9–22.

STEARN, W. T. 1990. John Lindley (1799–1865). A sketch of the life and works of a pioneer British orchidologist and gardener-botanist. In S. Sprunger (ed.), *Orchids from the Botanical Register, 1815–1847*: 15–44.

STEARN, W. T. 1992. Bauer, Ferdinand Lucas. In J. Kerr (ed.), *Dictionary of Australian Artists to 1870*: 53–54.

THISELTON-DYER, W. T. 1891. Historical account of Kew to 1891. *Kew Bulletin* 1891: 279–327.

WILLIS, G. M. & HOWES, F. N. 1950. Notes on early Kew and the King of Hanover. *Kew Bulletin* 1950: 299–318.

# Further reading

for *The structure and function of orchid flowers*

BAUER, F. & LINDLEY, J. 1830–38. *Illustrations of Orchidaceous Plants*. London.

BECHTEL, H., CRIBB, P. & LAUNERT, E. 1992. *The Manual of cultivated Orchid Species*. 3rd edn. London.

DE VOGEL, E. F. 1969. Monograph of the tribe *Apostasieae* (Orchidaceae). *Blumea* 17 (2): 315–50.

DRESSLER, R. L. 1981. *The Orchids: Natural history and Classification*. Cambridge, Massachusetts.

DRESSLER, R. L. 1983. Classification of the Orchidaceae and their probable origin. *Telopea* 2(4): 413–24.

GARAY, L. A. 1980. A generic revision of *Spiranthinae*. *Botanical Museum Leaflets, Harvard University*, 28(4): 277–425.

PRIDGEON, A. (ed.) 1992. *An Illustrated Encyclopaedia of Orchids*. Sydney, New South Wales.

SEIDENFADEN, G. & WOOD, J. J. 1992. *The Orchids of Peninsular Malaysia and Singapore*. Fredensborg, Denmark.

# Further reading

for *A selection of Franz Bauer's orchid paintings*

BECHTEL, H., CRIBB, P. & LAUNERT, E. 1992. *The Manual of cultivated Orchid Species*. 3rd edn, London.

BUTTLER, K. P. 1991. *Field Guide to Orchids of Britain and Europe*. Swindon.

CLEMENTS, M. A. 1989. *Catalogue of Australian Orchidaceae*. Australian Orchid Research Volume 1. Canberra.

COATS, A. M. 1969. *The Quest for Plants*. London.

CORRELL, D. S. 1950. *Native Orchids of North America*. Waltham, Massachusetts.

CRIBB, P. J. 1987. *The Genus Paphiopedilum*. Kew and London.

DARWIN, C. 1888. *The various Contrivances by which Orchids are fertilised by Insects*. 2nd edn, London.

DAVIES, P., DAVIES, J. & HUXLEY, A. J. 1983. *Wild Orchids of Britain and Europe*. London.

DRESSLER, R. L. 1981. *The Orchids: Natural History and Classification*. Cambridge, Massachusetts.

DUPUY, D. & CRIBB, P. 1988. *The Genus Cymbidium*. London.

JONES, D. L. 1988. *Native Orchids of Australia*. Frenchs Forest, New South Wales.

KAISER, R. 1993. *The Scent of Orchids*. Basel, Switzerland.

LANDWEHR, J. 1982. *Les Orchidées sauvages de France et d'Europe*. 2 vols. Lausanne.

LINDLEY, J. 1830–40. *The Genera and Species of Orchidaceous Plants*. London (reprinted by Asher, Amsterdam, 1963).

LINNAEUS, C. 1745. *Olandska och Gothlandska Resa ... forr attad Ahr 1741*. Stockholm (English translation by Maria Asberg & W. T. Stearn in Biological Journal, Linnean Soc. 5:1–107; 1973).

LUER, C. A. 1975. *The native Orchids of the United States and Canada, excluding Florida*. New York.

NICHOLLS, W. H. 1969. *Orchids of Australia*. Melbourne, Victoria.

NILSSON, S. 1979. *Orchids of Northern Europe*. Harmondsworth, Middlesex.

SUMMERHAYES, V. S. 1951. *Wild Orchids of Britain*. London.

VEITCH, J. & SONS. 1887–94. *A Manual of Orchidaceous Plants*. London (published in ten parts).

WOOLCOCK, C. & WOOLCOCK, D. 1984. *Australian terrestrial Orchids*. Melbourne, Victoria.

# Index

*Aceras* 116
  *A. anthropophorum* 42, 130
adder's tongue 106
*Aerides* 54
  *A. cornuta see A. odorata*
  *A. odorata* 36, 40
Aiton, William Townsend 14, 16, 39, 46, 48, 62, 64, 72, 100, 108, 136
*Anacamptis pyramidalis* 44
Anderson, Alexander 108
Andrews, Henry Charles 13
Anguillara 10
Anne, Queen 106
*Apostasia* 22
  *A. nuda* 26
  *A. wallichii* 26
*Apostaciaceae* 26
*Apostasioideae* 26
*Asclepiadaceae* 12

Baker, Elizabeth 18
Banks, Sir Joseph 9, 11–12, 13, 15, 16, 18, 19, 36, 39, 40, 50, 54, 62, 70, 90
Banks, Lady 28, 72
Bauer, Ferdinand Lucas 7–8, 9–11, 12, 18
Bauer, Francis (Franz) Andreas
  and Joseph Jacquin 11–12
  and Sir Joseph Banks 11–12
  at Kew 12–14, 16–18
  family background 8
  in Vienna 8–9
  study of orchids 14–15
Bauer, Josef Anton 8–9
Bauer, Lucas 8
Bauer, Theresia 8
Bauhin, Jean and Caspar 10, 126
bee orchid 116, 118
Bentham, George 142

*Bletia purpurea* 22
  *B. tankervilleae see Phaius tancarvilleae*
Bligh, Vice Admiral William 48
blue Caladenia 92
Blume, Carl Ludwig 136
Blunt, Wilfrid 7
Boccius, Norbert 8, 9, 10
*Bonatea speciosa* 46
Bonato, Giuseppe Antonio 46
Boothby, Sir Brooke 148
*Botanical Register* 15, 40, 54, 112, 114
*Botanische Buchillustration* (Nissen) 7
Brasavola, Antonio Musa 48
Brass, William 50
*Brassavola* 48
  *B. cucullata* 48
  *B. nodosa* 48
*Brassia maculata* 50
British Museum 16
broad-leaved helleborine 84, 86
*Broughtonia sanguinea* 19, 20
Brown, Robert 12, 14, 15, 16, 19, 39, 48, 50, 54, 64, 78, 92, 94, 100, 106, 108
burnt orchid 132

*Caladenia* 92
  *C. caerulea* 39, 92
*Calanthe* 136
Calcutta Botanical Garden 40, 136
Caley, George 80
*Calycanthus praecox see Chimonanthus praecox*
*Catasetum macrocarpum* 52
Cesalpino 10
*Chamorchis* 116
Chandler and Buckingham, Messrs 64
Charlotte, Queen 13, 16
*Chimonanthus praecox* 12

*Cleisostoma paniculatum* 39, 54
Clift, William 16
clown spikes 126
cockleshell orchid 82
*Codex Vindobonensis (Codex Aniciae Iulianae)* 10
*Coeloglossum viride* 56
Collinson, Peter 104
*Coloured Engravings of Heaths* (Andrews) 13
Columna, Fabius 10
Cook, Captain James 11
*Corallorhiza* 116
creeping lady's tresses 94
Cribb, P. 20
*Criosanthes* 64
  *C. plectrochilon* 64
Cumberland, Duke of 16
Cuming, Hugh 112
*Curtis's Botanical Magazine* 46, 68, 134, 146
*Cymbidium* 58
  *C. aloifolium* 58
  *C. ensifolium* 14, 60
*Cynosorchis morio see Orchis morio*
*Cypripedioideae* 28
*Cypripedium* 28, 66, 134
  *C. acaule* 62
  *C. album see C. reginae*
  *C. arietinum* 64
  *C. calceolus* 24, 66, 70, 72
  *C. parviflorum* 68
  *C. pubescens* 68, 70
  *C. reginae* 28, 72
  *C. spectabile see C. reginae*

Darwin, Charles 52
*Delineations of Exotick Plants Cultivated in the Royal Gardens at Kew* (Bauer) 13

*Dendrobium* 74
  *D. linguiforme* 39, 74
  *D. moniliforme* 74
  *D. speciosum* 39, 76
  *D. squalens* see *Xylobium variegatum*
Dietrichstein, Count 9
Dioscorides 9–10, 94, 128
*Dipodium* 78
  *D. punctatum* 39, 78
*Diuris aurea* 39, 80
  *D. sulphurea* 39, 80
Dodoens, Rembert 10
Drake, Miss 15
Dressler, R. L. 20, 82
Dryander, Jonas 9, 11, 62
Dunsterville 150

Edwards, Sydenham 7
Ehret, G. D. 11
Elcock, Edward 100
Elizabeth, Princess 13
*Encyclia* 82
  *E. cochleata* 82
  *E. fragrans* 82
Epidendroideae 20, 3?
*Epidendrum* 82
  *E. aloifolium* see *Cymbidium aloifolium*
  *E. coccineum* see *Maxillaria coccinea*
  *E. cucullatum* see *Brassavola cucullata*
  *E. elongatum* 34
  *E. lineare* see *Isochilus linearis*
  *E. sanguineum* see *Broughtonia sanguinea*
  *E. tessellatum* see *Vanda tessellata*
*Epipactis africana* 84
  *E. gigantea* 84
  *E. helleborine* 84, 86
  *E. palustris* 24, 88
*Erica* 13
*Eucalyptus* 78

fairy orchid 92
Fitch, W. H. 12
Flinders, Matthew 12
*Flora Americae Septentrionalis* (Pursh) 13
*Flora Australiensis* (Bentham) 142
*Flora Austriacae* (Jacquin) 39, 96
*Flora Caroliniana* (Walter) 72
*Flora Cochinchinensis* (Loureiro) 136
*Flora Graeca* (Sibthorp and Smith) 10
*Flora Lapponica* (Linnaeus) 66
*Flore de la Guyane Française* (Lémée) 82
fly orchid 124
Fothergill, John 14, 60
fox tail orchid 40
frog orchid 56

Frost, John 146

*Galearis spectabilis* 90
Garay, L. A. 150
*Gasteria* 134
Gauci, M. 15, 26
*Genera Filicum* (Hooker) 12
George III, King 13, 16, 18
Gerard, John 98, 106
Ghini, Luca 10
Glasgow Botanic Garden 68
*Glossodia* 92
  *G. major* 39, 92
  *G. minor* 92
golden donkey orchid 80
Goodyer, John 94
*Goodyera* 94
  *G. pubescens* 94
  *G. repens* 94
Göttingen University Library 16, 39, 96, 100, 108
Granville, A. B. 16
greater butterfly orchid 138
green fringed orchid 140
green-veined orchid 126
green-winged orchid 126
Greene, E. L. 9
Guelph, Ernest Augustus Frederick *see* Cumberland, Duke of

*Habenaria* 46, 138, 140
Hamilton, William 62
*Hammarbya* 116
Harrison, Richard 112
Hawkins, John 10
*Heathery, or a Monograph of the Genus Erica* (Andrews) 13
*Herminium* 116
Herschel, Sir John 144
*Himantoglossum hircinum* 39, 96, 98
Home, Sir James Everard 12, 15, 16
Hooker, Joseph 52
Hooker, William 13–14
Hooker, Sir William Jackson 12, 13, 68, 82, 134, 146
hornet orchid 80
Horticultural Society of London *see* Royal Horticultural Society
*Hortus Indicus Malabaricus* (Rheede tot Draakestein) 58
*Hortus Kewensis* (Aiton) 14, 39, 48, 62, 64, 72, 100, 108, 136

*Icones Plantarum Rariorum* (Jacquin) 9, 148

*Iconum Botanicarum Index Locupletissimus* (Pritzel) 7
*Illustrations of Orchidaceous Plants* (Bauer) 15, 19, 22, 26, 32, 39, 54, 114
*Iris* 22
*Isochilus* 100
  *I. linearis* 100

Jacquin, Joseph Franz 11, 12, 18
Jacquin, Nicolaus von, Baron 9, 10, 11, 39, 96, 100, 108, 148

Kaiser, Roman 98
Ker, John Bellenden 54
Kew *see* Royal Botanic Gardens, Kew
king orchid 76

lady orchid 128, 130
lady's slipper 66
large twayblade 104
large yellow lady's slipper 70
late spider orchid 120, 122
*Lectures on Comparative Anatomy* (Home) 15
Lémée 82
lesser butterfly orchid 138
Liechtenstein, Prince of 8
Liechtensteinische Bibliothek 8
lily-leaved twayblade 104
*Limodorum abortivum* 39, 102
Lindley, John 15, 16, 19, 40, 54, 72, 110, 112, 114, 128, 136, 150
Linnaeus, Carl 46, 48, 58, 60, 66, 72, 82, 90, 116, 126, 128, 132
Linnean Society (London) 18
*Liparis* 116
  *L. lilifolia* 104
  *L. loeselii* 104
Lister, Martin 106
*Listera* 106, 116
  *L. ovata* 106
lizard orchid 96, 98
Loddiges, Conrad (and Sons, nurserymen) 58, 112, 140, 150
London Medico-Botanical Society 146
London University 15
Loureiro, João 40, 136
Lysaght, A. M. 11

*Malaxis* 116
man orchid 42, 130
*Maranta* 10
Maria Theresia, Empress 9

marsh helleborine 88
Masson, Francis 13, 90
Mattioli, Pierandrea 10
mauve sleekwort 104
*Maxillaria* 110, 150
  *M. coccinea* 39, 108
  *M. subulata* 110
  *M. variegata see Xylobium variegatum*
Meynell, G. 12
military orchid 128
Miller, Philip 68, 72
monkey goblet 52
monkshead 52

*Narcissus* 22
Natural History Museum (London) 12,
  16, 39, 96, 100
*Neottia* 116
  *N. speciosa see Stenorrhynchos speciosum*
*Neuwiedia* 26
Nissen, Claus 7
Northumberland, Duke of 50

*Odontoglossum crispum* 14
*Oncidium* 112
  *O. altissimum* 114
  *O. ampliatum* 112
  *O. baueri* 39, 114
  *O. divaricatum* 112
  *O. harrisonianum* 112
  *O. pulvinatum* 112
  *O. sphegiferum* 112
*Ophrys* 116, 118, 122, 124
  *O. × albertiana* 120
  *O. apifera* 116, 118
  *O. fuciflora see O. holoserica*
  *O. holoserica* 120, 122
  *O. insectifera* 124
× *Orchiaceras macra* 130
*Orchidaceae* 7, 12, 14, 128
*Orchideenbuch* (Stein) 134
*Orchidoideae* 30
orchids
  anther and pollinia 22
  classification 26–36
  fruit and seeds 24
  orchid beetle 76
  ovary 22
  pollen 19
  pollination by bees 52, 76, 116, 118
  pollination by butterflies 44
  pollination by gnats 142
  pollination by moths 48, 138, 140
  pollination by spiders 88
  pollination by wasps 84, 124

role of fungi 24, 78, 102
structure and function of flowers 19–36
*see also* under individual genera and
  species
*Orchis* 90, 128, 130
  *O. chlorantha see Platanthera chlorantha*
  *O. militaris* 128
  *O. morio* 126
  *O. odori hirci see Himantoglossum hirci*
  *O. purpurea* 39, 128, 130
  *O. spectabilis see Galearis spectabilis*
  *O. ustulata* 132
*Ornithidium coccineum see Maxillaria*
  *coccinea*
*Orobanchaceae* 102
Osbeck, Pehr 60
*Osmunda regalis* 72
*Österreichische Bibliothek* 10

*Paphiopedilum* 28, 134
  *P. venustum* 134
*Paradisus Londinensis* (Salisbury) 13
Parkinson, Sydney 11
parson-in-the-pulpit 92
Paterson, Colonel William 39, 80
Pavon y Jiminez, José 110, 150
Pfitzer, E. H. H. 134
*Phaius* 136
  *P. flavus* 136
  *P. grandifolius see P. tancarvilleae*
  *P. maculatus see P. flavus*
  *P. tancarvilleae* 14, 136
*Phragmipedium* 28, 134
pink hyacinth orchid 78
pink lady's slipper 62
pink moccasin flower 62
*Platanthera* 138
  *P. bifolia* 138
  *P. chlorantha* 30, 138
  *P. lacera* 140
Pliny the Elder 116
Plumier, Charles 82, 108
Pridgeon, A. 20
Pritzel, Georg August 7
*Pterostylis* 142
  *P. rufa* 142
purple hooded orchis 90
purple scutcheon 104
Pursh, Frederick 13
pyramidal orchid 44

queen lady's slipper 72

Rafinesque-Schmaltz, C. S. 90

ragged fringed orchid 140
ram's head lady's slipper 64
Ray, John 106
Redouté, Antoine-Ferdinand 8
Redouté, Charles-Joseph 8
Redouté, Henri-Joseph 8
Redouté, Marguerite 8
Redouté, Pierre-Joseph 7
Rheede tot Draakestein, Henrik Adriaan
  var 58
*Rhizanthella* 102
  *R. gardneri* 78
Richard, Louis Claude 138, 148
rock orchid 76
Roxburgh, William 40
Royal Botanic Garden, Edinburgh 46
Royal Botanic Gardens, Kew 11, 12–14,
  16–18, 39, 66, 82, 88, 100, 110, 136
Royal Horticultural Society 15, 112, 114
Royal Society 18
  *Philosophical Transactions* 15
Ruiz Lopez, Hipolito 110, 150
rusty hood 142

Sainsbury, Sir Robert and Lady 66
Salisbury, Richard Anthony 13, 72
*Sarcanthus* 54
*Satyrium* 144
  *S. erectum* 39, 144
Scheer, Frederick 15, 16–18
Scheidel, Franz 96
*Second Parte of William Turner's Herball*
  (Turner) 86
Seidenfaden, G. 20
*Selectarum Stirpium Americanarum*
  *Historia* (Jacquin) 39, 100, 108
*Selenipedium* 28, 134
*Serapias* 86
Shi-kotei, Emperor 60
showy lady's slipper 72
showy orchis 90
Sibthorp, John 9–10
slipper orchids 28, 134
small yellow lady's slipper 68
Smith, J. E. 78, 80
Smith, John 16
Solander, Daniel 62
Sowerby, James 7, 136
*Species Plantarum* (Linnaeus) 48, 58, 66,
  82, 90, 116, 126, 132
spider orchid (*Brassia*) 50
spider orchid (*Caladenia*) 92
*Spiranthes* 94, 116, 148
  *S. speciosa see Stenorrhynchos speciosum*
*Spiranthoideae* 32
Stanhope, Philip Henry, Earl 146

*Stanhopea* 146
  *S. insignis* 146
Stearn, W. T. 11, 15
Stein 134
*Stenorrhynchos* 148
  *S. speciosum* 32, 148
*Strelitzia* 13
  *S. reginae* 13
*Strelitzia Depicta* (Bauer) 13
Swartz, Olof 58, 144
sweethearts 106
Swieten, Gerard van 9

tadpole orchid 96, 98
*Testiculis hirci see Himantoglossum
  hircinum*
  *T. morionis see Orchis morio*

*Thesaurus Literaturae Botanicae* (Pritzel) 7
*Thuja* 64
Thunberg, Carl Peter 46
tiger orchid 80
tongue orchid 74
*Tragorchis see Himantoglossum hircinum*
Turner, William 10, 86
Turpin, Pierre 7
twayblade 106

*Vanda* 54
  *V. tessellata* 36
*Vandoideae* 20, 36
*Vanilla* 26
Victoria, Queen 16
Vienna Botanic Garden 9
violet limodore 102

Wallich, Dr Nathaniel 134, 136
Walter, Thomas 72
wax lip orchid 92
Westmacott, Richard Jr 18
white lady's slipper 72
Willdenow, C. L. 46
Wood, J. J. 20

*Xylobium* 150
  *X. squalens see X. variegatum*
  *X. variegatum* 150

yellow bee 112
yellow moccasin flower 70
Young, William 72